Spotlight SCIENCE

FOR SCOTLAND

S2

★ Keith JOHNSON   ★ Gareth WILLIAMS
★ Sue ADAMSON   ★ Derek McMONAGLE

With the active support of: Lawrie Ryan, Bob Wakefield,
Anne Goldsworthy, Roger Frost, Helen Davis, Valerie Wood-Robinson,
Phil Bunyan, John Bailey, Adrian Wheaton,
Janet Hawkins, Ann Johnson, Graham Adamson, Diana Williams.

5-14 EDITION

First published in 2002 by:
Nelson Thornes Ltd
Delta Place
27 Bath Road
CHELTENHAM
GL53 7TH
United Kingdom

03 04 05 06 / 10 9 8 7 6 5 4 3 2

A catalogue record for this book is available from the British Library

ISBN 0 7487 7055 0

Illustrations by Jane Cope and Barking Dog Art
Page make-up by Tech-set

Printed and bound in China by Sun Fung

Acknowledgements

The authors and publishers are grateful to the following for permission to reproduce photographs:

Ace Picture Library: Laszlo Willinger 174T, Roger Howard 196T; Action Plus: 94T, 157TR, TL, Glyn Kirk 174BR; Adams Picture Library: 126TL, TR; AES Educational: 145B; Alamy Images: Image State, Geoff De Feu 30MB, Pictor International 97; Al Hamdan: 77BL; Allsport: Gray Mortimore 40T; Ardea: C&J Knights 27T, 194h; Axon Images: 50ML, MCL, 82BR, 145M, 169TR; Biophoto Associates: 28B, 139B; BOC Group: 165M; British Film Institute: 20T; British Steel: 73T; Bruce Coleman: 116M, 118BL, Frank Greenaway 133ML, Hans Reinhard 180BL; ColPal: 194g; Collections: 165BR, 169B; Camera Press London: Neil Morrison; Colorsport: 94BL, 197B; CF Nolke: 79M; Corel (NT): 10T, 11M, 14TL, 17MB, B, 18T, B, 22M, 27BR, 28T, 29, 32, 35B, 50T, MCR, MR 52B, 53T, MB, B, 58T, 69, 72TCL, 80BCR, 92M, 94ML, 95TR, B, 96, 110, 112, 116T, 118BR, 121, 147, 160R, 163B, 164R, 178, 181, 183T, 215L; Digital Vision (NT): 4MC, BMR, 11T, 16T, 21T, 117T, 133MR, 161M, 176T, B, 184T, 185; Edinburgh Zoo: 20B; Empics: John Marsh 94BR, Tony Marshall 156; Eric Hayman: 48TR; Frank Lane Picture Agency: Hannu Hautala 30MT, R Wilmshurst 90BL, R Bender 180BR; Galapagos Travel: 30B; Gene Cox: 114B; Geological Museum London: 46T; Geoscience Features Picture Library: 20M, 46MC, 59BR, 60, 72M, 73B, 120; Getty Images: Stone, Bob Torrez 33, Chad Slattery 55, L A Peck 173; Grabber Handwarmers: 197TML; Greenpeace: 4ML; Griffin: 205; GT Insulations: 90BR; Hi-Test Photo: 79B; Holt Studios International: N Cattlin 4BL, 9B, 76T; Hot Hands: 197TL; ICI: 10B, 25B, 52T; Illustrated London News: 161BC; Image Library (NT): 84BR, 164L; Image State: 43; Impact Photos: 80M, 186T, Alain Le Garsmeur 82TL, TR; John Birdsall Photography: 140B; John Foxx (NT): 80T; J Moss: 170M; J P Fankhauser: 87; J V DeFord Jr: 92L; Kemira Agro UK: 201; Kanehara & Co. Ltd: 126M (Ishihara's tests for colour blindness cannot be conducted with this material); Leslie Garland Picture Library: 35ML; Magnum Photos: W Eugene Smith 9T; Mahaux Photography: 61; Martyn Chillmaid: 4MR, 11B, 14TC, TR, 15T, 25T, 36, 38T, B, 40B, 46ML, MR, B, 47ML, MC, MR, TL, 48B, 49, 54R, M, L, 56, 63, 68, 70, 71, 74B, M, 78M, 80BL, BCL, BR, B, 81, 82BL, BC, 83, 84BL, BC, 85, 90T, 93MR, 95TL, 97TL, 100, 101T, M, B, 102, 103TL, BL, TR, BR, 107, 109M, B, 118T, 119, 123, 128, 130, 132M, 137, 139T, 144T, B, 148, 149, 160L, ML, MR, 161BL, BR, 162TL, TR, BL, BR, T, M, 165BL, BC, 166R, M, L, 168, 169TL, ML, MR, 170T, B, 171, 172, 174BL, 175, 180T, 186b, cL, cR, d, e, f, g, h, i, j, B,188, 189L, M, R, 190T, B, 191L, M, R, B, 192L, R, 194a, b, c, d, e, f, 196B, 197TR, 199, 202, 204, 210; Mary Evans Picture Library: 30T, 44T, 47T, 66BL, 86, A Muttit 13B, Devany 216; Mike Read: 6; Milepost 9½: British Rail Archive 162TC; NASA: 133TR, 200; National Museums of Scotland: 19; Natural Visions: 13TR, TL, 22TR, BR, 113; News International: Michael Powell 4T; Nick Cobbing: 183M, B; Oxford Scientific Films: 22TCL, BL, 27BL, 66BR, 117B, K A Larsson 5T, P Gathercole 13MR, Colin Milkins 13BL, J A L Cooke 13BR, John McCammon 16B, Kim Weserskov 17T, Doug Allen 17MT, Alan Root 31, G I Bernard 116BL; Panos Pictures: Glenn Edwards 58B, Sean Sprague 59BL; Papilio: Robert Gill 94MR; PepsiCo International: 159; Peter Fraekel: 59M; Phillip Allen Publishers: 135; Photodisc (NT): 5B, 8T, 12T, 22TL, 26, 72TCR, 97TR, 133BL, BR, 206; Planet Earth Pictures: N Downer 4BR, F C Millington 8B, Barry Gorman 154; Porsche: 72L; Proctor & Gamble: 84T, 187; Raleigh: 35TR; Rex Features: Jonathon Player 182T; Riverford Organic Vegetables: 193; Robert Harding Picture Library: M Leslie Evans 195B; Royal Botanical Gardens Edinburgh: 21B; Russel Knightly Media: 146; Science Photolibrary: 138BL, BR, 141, 177R, 182B, Martin bond 15M, 214, Martin Dohrn 35MR, G Williams 93ML, John Mead 111, PSU Entomology 116BR, Oscar Burriel 124, Dr Gopal Murti 140T, Saturn Stills 145T, R Folwell 161T, Adam Hart Davis 165T, CNRI 176B, G Tompkinson 198B, S Fraser 212, Alfred Pasieka 219; Science Museum London: 44B; Scottish HydroElectric: 97BR; Scottish Road Safety Campaign: 77T; Shout Pictures: 132TL, TR, 133TL; Sporting Pictures: 151; S Marks: 138T; T Hill: 15B, 197TC; Topham Picture Point: 90BC, 167, 177L, 195T, 198T, 203; Transport Research Laboratory: 39; Trumpf: 53M; Wadworth & Co. Ltd: 76B

Picture research by johnbailey@axonimages.com and Stuart Sweatmore. Every effort has been made to trace all copyright holders but if any have been overlooked the publisher will be pleased to make the necessary arrangements at the first opportunity.

Contents

Against all odds

This little boy stood for hours in the cold in London:
He wanted to tell people what had happened to his local river.

What do you think could have happened to the river**?**

This is just one example of **pollution**.
What do you think we mean by pollution**?**
Write down some of your ideas.

Pollution is when we do things that harm our environment.

What's causing the pollution?

Look at these photographs:

▶ Copy the list below of the types of pollution shown in the photographs.
Match each one with the correct effects from the other list:

Type of pollution	**Effects of pollution**
• dumping radioactive waste	• damages body cells
• oil spills	• lung diseases
• dangerous tips	• kills trees and water life
• smog	• kills sea-birds
• detergents	• harmful chemicals leak out
• acid gases	• too many water plants grow

Signs of pollution

When fossil fuels burn, they make acid gases like **sulphur dioxide**.
These dissolve in water in the clouds to make acid rain.
Acid rain can kill plants and fish.

Black spot is a mould that grows on
roses. The mould cannot live if
there is sulphur dioxide in the air.

a What does it tell you if roses do
not have black spot**?**

Lichens are plants that are sensitive to
sulphur dioxide in the air.

b Look at the shrubby lichens
in the picture.
What do you think the air is like**?**

Who says the rain's to blame?

Does acid rain really damage plants?

Plan an investigation to see how acid affects the growth of cress seeds.

- What will you change?
- How will you make it a fair test?
- What will you measure to see if the seeds have grown?
- Your investigation should last about a week. How often will you record your results?

Show your plan to your teacher before you try it out.

No real answer

In Sweden, they are fighting acid rain by spraying lime on lakes.

c What do you think the lime does to the acid?

Experts say that it is "like taking aspirin to cure cancer".

d What do you think the experts mean by this?

e What would be a better way to cure acid rain?

1 Copy and complete:
Pollution occurs when . . . . put harmful . . . . or energy into the . . . . When fossil fuels are burned, they give off gases like . . . . These gases dissolve in water to give . . . . The effects of acid rain can be reduced by adding . . . . to lakes.

2 Each day millions of cars pour poisonous exhaust fumes into the atmosphere. Pollutants in the fumes include lead, carbon monoxide and nitrogen oxides.
a) Try to find out what effects these chemicals have on our bodies.
b) How can these chemicals be reduced in exhaust fumes?

3 Why do you think that people in Norway blame factories in Britain for acid rain pollution?
How could our factories give out less sulphur dioxide?

4 Why do oil slicks appear on the sea? What effect does oil have on sea-birds and other coastal life?
How are oil slicks treated to make them less harmful?

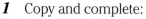

Things to do

Exploring pyramids

Food chains can show how food (and energy) pass from one living thing to another.

Write out this food chain in the correct order:
owl, oak leaves, shrew, caterpillar

a Where do the oak leaves get their energy from**?**

How many?

Food chains cannot tell you **how many** living things are involved.
It takes lots of leaves to feed a caterpillar, and lots of caterpillars to feed one shrew.

▶ Look at the diagram:

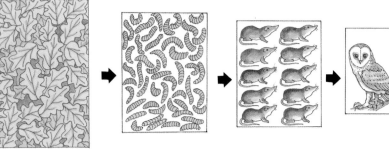

b Why are there more plants than there are herbivores**?**

c Why are there more prey than there are predators**?**

Up the pyramids

Look at the numbers in this food chain:

owl	1
shrews	10
caterpillars	100
oak leaves	300

You can show this information in a **pyramid of numbers**.
The area of each box tells us how big the numbers are.
Start with the plants on the first level and build it up:

level 4
level 3
level 2
level 1

▶ Copy the diagram and label each feeding level.

d What happens to the **numbers** of living things as you go up this pyramid**?**

e What happens to the **size** of each living thing as you go up this pyramid**?**

f Why are the plants always on the first level**?**

▶ Now try drawing a pyramid of numbers for each of these food chains:

	producer	*herbivore*	*carnivore*	*top carnivore*
g	5 cabbages	20 slugs	5 thrushes	1 cat
h	1 oak tree	100 caterpillars	5 robins	100 fleas

A top carnivore

Funnel fun

You can find very small animals in leaf litter using a **Tullgren funnel**.

Phew!... too hot and dry up there for me.

- Set up the funnel as shown:
- Place a sample of leaf litter onto the gauze.
- Switch on the light and leave it for 30 minutes to work.
- ***Be careful not to over-heat your sample and kill your animals.***
- Use a lens to look at the tiny animals that you have collected.

i What two things made the animals move downwards?

j Why should the light not be too close to your leaf litter?

k Why should your layer of leaf litter not be too thick?

Your teacher can give you a Help Sheet to identify your animals. It also tells you what they eat.

- Make a count of each of your animals and record it in a table:

Animal	Number found	Herbivore or carnivore?
mites springtails symphylids		

- Draw a pyramid of numbers for the animals you have collected.

Things to do

1 Copy and complete:
Pyramids of . . . . can tell us about the numbers of living things at each feeding . . . . Plants are always put in the . . . . level because they make food by . . . . and so bring energy into the food chain. As you go up the pyramid, the numbers of animals get . . . . and the size of each animal gets . . . .

2 a) Draw a pyramid of numbers from these data:

  sparrowhawk   1
  blue tits   5
  bark beetles 50
  beech tree   1

b) How is it that one tree can support so many herbivores?

c) Why do you think this is called an 'inverted pyramid'?

3 Instead of using numbers to draw pyramids, scientists sometimes use **biomass**. This is the mass of living material.

a) What would the pyramid of numbers in question 2 look like as a pyramid of biomass?

b) Draw and label it.

4 Look at the Help Sheet that you used in the activity on this page.
Choose 5 of the animals and make a key that you could use to identify each one. Get a friend to try it out.

Dicing with death

Pesticides are chemicals that farmers use to kill **pests**.

a What kinds of plants and animals might be pests to a farmer?

b Why do you think farmers need to kill pests?

The main farm pests are insects, weeds and moulds.
Farmers need to control them because they destroy crops.

Nasty stuff

DDT is a pesticide. Only a small amount is needed to kill *any* insect.
It was used to kill plant pests and the mosquitoes that spread **malaria**.
However, DDT does not break down quickly. It stays in the soil for
a long time. So it can be passed along food chains. This is dangerous.

This lake in California was sprayed with DDT to control midges.
Look at the diagram to see what happened:

c How does DDT get into this food chain?

d What happens to the concentration of DDT as it passes along
the food chain? Try to explain this.

e Why are the fish-eating birds the first to be killed by DDT?

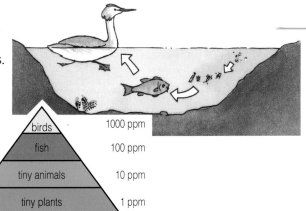

birds	1000 ppm
fish	100 ppm
tiny animals	10 ppm
tiny plants	1 ppm

pyramid of numbers

Who killed the sparrowhawk?

In the 1960s, seeds were often dipped in pesticide to protect them from pests.
Soon birds of prey, like the sparrowhawk, started dying.
Their bodies had large amounts of pesticide in them.
They also laid eggs with thin shells.

f How do you think the pesticide got from the seeds into the sparrowhawk?

g Why was it less concentrated in the bodies of seed-eating birds?

h Why do more birds die if their eggs have thin shells?

Pesticides, like DDT, are now banned in many countries.

The perfect pesticide?

A pesticide must be effective, but it must also be safe.
Discuss, in your groups, what makes a good pesticide.

- Which insects should it kill?
- For how long should it be active?
- Should it dissolve in water? Why?
- How will it get into the insect's body?
- On which part of the body will it act?
- How will it be safely used?

Write down your ideas.

Disaster in Minamata

Minamata is a fishing village in Japan. In 1953 there was a disaster. Fifty people died and hundreds were very ill. They were poisoned by mercury.

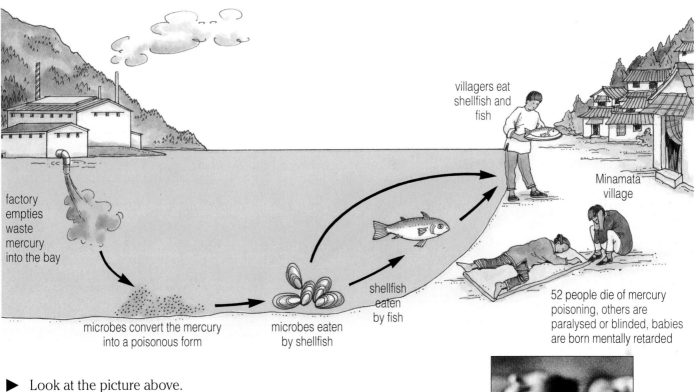

villagers eat shellfish and fish

Minamata village

factory empties waste mercury into the bay

microbes convert the mercury into a poisonous form

microbes eaten by shellfish

shellfish eaten by fish

52 people die of mercury poisoning, others are paralysed or blinded, babies are born mentally retarded

▶ Look at the picture above.

i Where did the mercury come from**?**

j How do you think the mercury got into the food chain**?**

k Explain why the concentration of mercury was higher in the people than in the fish.

l What parts of the body are most affected by mercury poisoning**?**

Things to do

1 Copy and complete:
Chemicals that kill pests are called . . . . Pests that can damage crops are . . . . , moulds and . . . . Some pesticides do not . . . . down easily. They can enter food . . . . and, as they are passed on, they become . . . . concentrated. Animals at the . . . . of the food chain are the first ones to die.

2 A new pesticide has been made to kill weeds.
The manufacturer wants to know at what concentration to sell it.
If it is too strong, it will kill the crop and harm wildlife.
If it is too weak, then it will not kill the weeds.
Plan an investigation to find out the best concentration of pesticide.

3 Some insects can develop **resistance** to a particular pesticide.
a) What is likely to happen to the farmer's crop if this happens?
b) What could the farmer do about it?

4 In Holland, they are using ladybirds to kill off lice on trees. The ladybirds are imported from California. Sixty million are being sold to Holland. The US suppliers say "Unlike pesticides, they are environmentally-friendly and real cute too!".
a) This is an example of **biological control**.
What do you think this means?
b) What are the advantages of using ladybirds instead of pesticides?

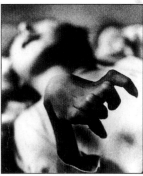

Cycles

Can you remember what happens to dead plants and animals?
They rot away. We say that they **decompose**.
The microbes that make dead things rot are called **decomposers**.
The most important microbes are **fungi** (moulds) and **bacteria**.

▶ Look at the diagram:

a How do plants take up nutrients?

b How do nutrients get into animals?

c How do nutrients get back into the soil?

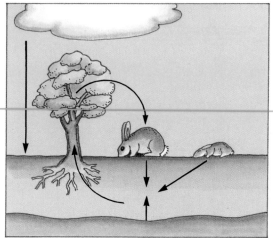

The natural roundabout

When plants and animals die, they decompose.
Nutrients are then put back into the soil.
Without fungi and bacteria, the dead material would never
decompose.

▶ Look at the diagram:

d Which process makes soil nutrients part of green plants?

e What are the living things that return nutrients to the soil?

We call the movement of nutrients a **nutrient cycle**.
This takes place on land, in fresh-water and in the sea.

f Where do you think the decomposers are found in the sea?

g Can you name 3 of the most important nutrients?

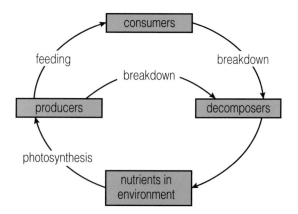

Natural or chemical?

Chemical fertilisers contain the nutrients **nitrogen**, **phosphorus**
and **potassium**. They are easy to store and to use. The farmer also
knows exactly how much of each nutrient is being used. However,
sometimes chemical fertilisers get washed out of the soil into rivers.
Some farmers prefer to use **natural fertilisers** like manure. They
rot down slower and add **humus** to the soil to improve it.

h Can you give 2 advantages of organic fertilisers?

i Can you give 2 advantages of chemical fertilisers?

Breaking the cycle

Humans share the Earth with millions of other living things. Unfortunately some human activities destroy wildlife. They disrupt the natural cycle of life that keeps environments in balance.

- Pollution can harm our environment in many ways.
- Clearing land for crops, housing, roads, factories and mines destroys the habitats of plants and animals.
- Over-fishing can cause the collapse of fish stocks.
- Hunters and poachers are threatening the survival of rare species.

Do some research into ways in which we can protect living things and their environments.
You could find information in books, ROMs or on the internet.

Make a leaflet aimed at convincing others of the need to protect the environment.

Your ideas should:

- be workable and able to be enforced;
- not threaten the livelihood of people, like fishermen;
- use the idea of **sustainable development**, such as replacing trees that have been felled for timber or not taking so many fish out of the oceans that they cannot be replaced by natural reproduction

---

1 Copy and complete:
Decomposers are microbes that . . . . down dead things. The most important decomposers are . . . . and bacteria. The nutrients in the soil are replaced when . . . . and animals die and . . . . Plants take up these nutrients and use them during . . . . Three important nutrients for plant growth are . . . . , phosphorus and . . . .

2 Recycling means using materials again.
a) Make a list of materials that can be recycled.
b) What effect could recycling of these materials have on:
  i) The raw materials used to manufacture goods?
  ii) The energy needed to manufacture these goods 'from scratch'?
  iii) Landfill sites?

3 35% of all our waste comes from packaging.
a) Make a list of the different types of packaging that we take away from shops.
b) In what ways does this packaging cause us problems?
Every year every person in the UK uses up one tree's worth of paper.
c) How would the recycling of paper help our environment?

4 Use books, ROMs or the internet to find out how the following help conservation in the UK:
a) National Nature Reserves (NNRs)
b) Sites of Special Scientific Interest (SSSIs).
c) Nitrate sensitive areas.
d) Heritage Coasts.
e) Set-aside.
f) Tree preservation orders.

Things to do

Poison algae

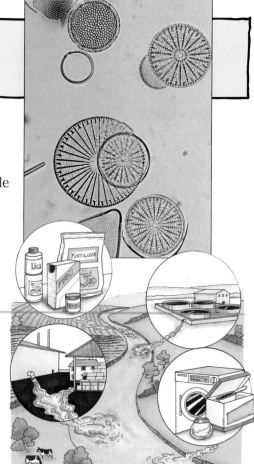

Algae are tiny plants. They live in lakes, rivers and seas.

Look at this food chain:

algae ➡ water fleas ➡ small fish ➡ large fish ➡ people

a Why are algae found at the start of the food chain**?**

b Can you name 3 things that algae need to grow**?**

c Why are fisheries often found where there are lots of algae**?**

Algae grow well when there is light, warmth and lots of **nutrients**.
Nutrients, like **nitrates** and **phosphates**, make algae grow best.

d What do you think will happen if *lots* of nutrients get into the water**?**

▶ Look at the picture:
Write down the ways in which *extra* nutrients get into the river.

Too much of a good thing

More nutrients mean more plant growth – in this case, lots of algae.
This can cause problems for animals and other plants in the water.

▶ Write out these sentences in the correct order.
They will tell you what can happen when too much algae grows.

Algae die and sink to the bottom of the lake or river.	Extra nutrients in the water make the algae grow fast.	The lack of oxygen in the water kills fish and other water animals.	Dead algae are broken down by microbes which use up lots of oxygen.

A soapy story

Detergents contain phosphates. These are plant nutrients.
In this experiment, you can find out the effect of detergent on the growth of algae.

- Label 6 test-tubes 1 to 6.
- Add 5 cm³ of nutrient solution to each tube.
- Using a clean dropper, add 5 drops of algae water to each tube.
- Using clean droppers, add the following amounts of detergent solution and distilled water.

Test-tube	Drops of detergent solution	Drops of distilled water
1	0	5
2	1	4
3	2	3
4	3	2
5	4	1
6	5	0

- Leave all 6 test-tubes in a well-lit place.
- After a few days, shake each tube and see how green it is.
  Compare the growth of algae in each one.
- Record your results in a table.
- Discuss your results and write down your conclusions.

Living indicators

We can use water animals to tell us how pure the water is:

- Come on in,
  the water's fine!

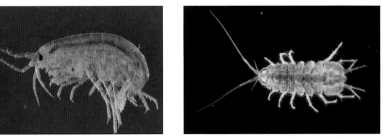

Mayfly larvae and stonefly larvae need clean water.

- It's getting worse!

Freshwater shrimps and water-lice can stand some pollution.

- The dirty duo!

Blood worms and sludge worms just love pollution!

e   If you find a stonefly larva in a water sample, what would it tell you about the water?

f   Which animals do you think could survive in the water in test-tube 6 in your investigation?

g   Can you think of any other ways of testing the water for pollution?

---

1   Copy and complete:
Algae are . . . . that live in water. To grow well, they need light, warmth and . . . .
Two of the nutrients which increase the growth of algae are . . . . and phosphates.
If too much algae grow, they die and . . . . rot them down. The microbes use up a lot of . . . . and this means that fish and other water animals will . . . .

2   Are farmers poisoning our water supply?
Some of the nitrates in fertilisers wash out of the soil and trickle down into the bed-rock.
Very slowly, the nitrates are moving nearer to water that we use to drink.
a)   Try to explain the 'nitrate time bomb'.
b)   Find out what effects nitrates can have on our health.

3   a)   Should chemical fertilisers be banned?
b)   What would happen to the world's food production if they were?
c)   What could we use instead of them if they were banned?

Clearing weeds from a canal

Things to do

The water cycle

What states of water can you see in each of the pictures?

▶

Water is one of the most important substances on the Earth.

Do you agree with Jack?
Write about 4 or 5 lines to explain why.

We use billions of litres of water every day.
Have you ever wondered why we don't run out of it?
The answer is that it is **recycled**.

The water cycle is a very important process in nature.

In your group make a poster to show the water cycle.
This picture could be the **_start_** of your poster.

The labels give information about some parts of the water cycle.
Add them to your picture in the right places.
Where is the rain likely to fall?
Draw it on your picture.
Make sure you put arrows on your picture to show which way the water is moving.

a Energy from the Sun is very important to the water cycle.
   Which part of the cycle does this affect?

b Why does water sometimes fall as **_snow_** rather than rain?

c What might cause impurities in the rain?

Labels
- water evaporates from the sea
- water as a gas (vapour) moves upwards
- as it gets colder, water condenses into droplets to form clouds
- wind moves clouds
- droplets get heavier, and water falls as rain, hail or snow
- the water returns to the sea through lakes and rivers

Before water goes back to the sea it is piped into our homes from lakes, rivers or from underground.
You couldn't drink water which came straight from rivers.

Why not?

All water must be cleaned before we can use it.
This happens at a water treatment plant (waterworks).
Very large amounts of water must be cleaned cheaply.
The process used is called **filtration**.

Would you like to drink this?

Cleaning water

Your teacher will give you some muddy water.
Your task is to get the cleanest water you can from the muddy water.
You can use any of the equipment your teacher will give you.

Draw a diagram of the arrangement you use to get the clean water.

You must not drink this water. Why not?

Find out how water is cleaned at a water treatment plant.

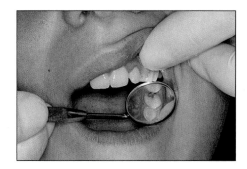

▶ In some areas sodium fluoride (NaF) is added to the water after it has been cleaned. Dentists think that this **fluoride** helps to stop tooth decay. However too much fluoride can be poisonous.
d Do you think fluoride should be added? Explain your views.
e Suggest other ways of reducing the decay of your teeth.

1 Imagine you are a water particle in a drop of rain. Write about your adventures as you pass through the water cycle. Finish your story when you reach the clouds again. Be sure to write about changes of state.

2 Draw a diagram of the apparatus used normally for filtration in the laboratory. Label the **residue** and **filtrate** on your diagram.

3 Design a piece of apparatus to measure rainfall. Your apparatus should be able to remain outdoors for long periods of time.

4 Will it rain for 40 days after a rainy St. Swithin's Day? There are lots of sayings about the weather. Use books and ask friends or relatives about these sayings. Write down as many as you can. Do you think there is truth in any of these?

5 Find out about **hard water**. What is the difference between **hard water** and **soft water**? Give one advantage and one disadvantage of living in a hard water area.

Things to do

Biology at Work

Deforestation

a What do you think we mean by the word 'deforestation'?

b Why do you think humans are cutting down and clearing large areas of tropical rainforest?
Try to think of **3** reasons.

Forests help to maintain the balance of the gases in the atmosphere.

c How do forests affect the carbon dioxide in the atmosphere?

d How do forests affect the oxygen in the atmosphere?

e What effect will deforestation have on the concentration of each of these gases in the atmosphere?

f Sustainable timber production could conserve our forests.
Give **2** ways in which this could happen.

Glasshouse production

To produce a high yield of crop, a grower needs photosynthesis to occur at maximum rate.

g What conditions are needed for photosynthesis?

▶ Look at the diagram of the glasshouse:

h How are the crops kept at the right temperature in the winter?

i Give **2** ways in which the temperature in the glasshouse is controlled in summer.

j How is the carbon dioxide concentration increased inside the glasshouse?

k How is the amount of sunlight inside the glasshouse controlled   i) in winter?   ii) in summer?

▶ Look at the photograph:

l How are crops watered in modern commercial glasshouses?

Conditions inside glasshouses allow plants to:
• grow earlier in the year,
• grow in places where they would not normally grow.

m How do these 2 things help the crop grower?

ventilation flaps restrict the temperature increase

shades restrict excessive sunlight

paraffin heater can provide heat and CO_2

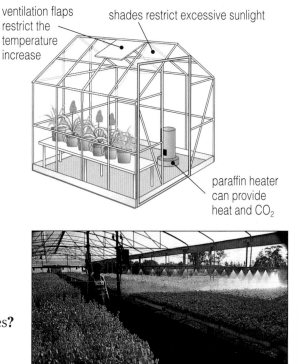

Fish farming

Many fish species are **over-fished** and some are at the point of extinction.

n Give *2* ways in which fishermen have become more efficient at catching fish.

International agreements could control the amount of fishing.

o What controls could be put into place?

Another answer to the over-fishing problem is **fish farming**. Fish, like salmon and trout, are kept in large cages.

p Why do you think the fish are:
   i) fed on a high protein diet?
   ii) treated with chemicals that kill microbes?
   iii) kept in cages that keep out other types of fish?

q There are worries that fish farming can cause pollution. How do you think this could happen?

Conservation

Zoos are able to breed wild animal species in captivity.

r How do you think that zoos are able to:
   i) increase the numbers of a particular species in the wild?
   ii) show people that wildlife is worth preserving?
   iii) research into the needs of wild species?

Many zoos have **captive breeding programmes** for endangered species.

s What do you think is involved in a captive breeding programme?

t Why is it important that zoos also *attract* people?

The Arabian Oryx has been bred in Phoenix Zoo and released into the wild.

Botanic gardens and seed banks
Scientists believe that 25% of the world's plant species could be extinct in the next 50 years.

u What are the main threats to plants in the wild?

v How can botanic gardens help conserve plant species?

Seed banks are cold stores of seeds.
The seeds can be kept at -40 °C for 200 years.

w How can this help conserve endangered plant species?

The Millennium Seed Bank has been constructed in the UK. The building stores seeds from about 10% of the world's estimated 250 000 wild flowering plants. The project stemmed from Britain's signing of the 1992 Convention of Biodiversity in Rio.

x Use books, ROMs and the internet to find out more about the Rio Convention.

Questions

1 Every year, 250 tonnes of lead from fishermen's weights gets into the environment.
It is thought that birds like the mute swan eat the lead weights when feeding.
a) How do you think the lead gets into the blood of the swan?
Swans in town areas are more affected by this type of poisoning than those in the country.
b) Why do you think this is?
c) How could this pollution be reduced without banning fishing altogether?

2 The following data were collected from a river:

pike	1
trout	10
water fleas	500
algae	10 000

a) Draw a pyramid of numbers (not to scale) for the river.
b) Which living thing would you remove if you wanted to increase the number of trout in the river?
c) Give one other effect of removing this living thing from the river.

3 Some DDT was sprayed on a lake to control mosquitoes.
Look at the table showing the amounts of DDT in a food chain.

cormorant	26.5 ppm
pike	1.3 ppm
minnow	0.2 ppm
algae	0.05 ppm
water	0.000 05 ppm

Explain how the cormorant has 500 000 times more DDT in its body than there is in the water.

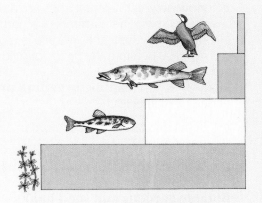

4 The Royal Society for the Protection of Birds has said that more than 40 bird species are threatened by intensive farming. Birds in decline on farmland include the skylark, barn owl, lapwing and golden eagle.
a) List the ways in which you think farming can reduce bird numbers.
b) What steps do you think could be taken to improve this situation?

5 Plan an investigation to find out how clean your local river is.
What evidence of pollution would you look for?
What chemicals would you test for, and how?
How could you use 'indicator animals' to tell you how clean the river is?

6 Decomposers, like fungi, are very useful in the environment.
Explain why plants and animals depend upon them so much.

Populations

Many different kinds of animals and plants lived on the Earth and disappeared long before people evolved.

It is not always easy to understand why some organisms have survived whilst others have become extinct. Factors like being able to adapt to a changing climate, the availability of food and the ability to compete successfully play an important part.

It remains to be seen whether people will survive for many millions of years to come or whether we are just a dead end in the great process of evolution.

Here today and gone tomorrow?

There have been many species of animals and plants that used to live on the Earth but they don't exist any more. What happened to them all? They have become **extinct**.

▶ What would it be like if we really could climb up a massive fern-like tree to watch a herd of grazing brontosaurus, perhaps gaze up at a passing pterodactyl or hide in terror from a marauding tyrannosaurus?

Film-maker's impression of a flying Pterodactyl

Sadly, this is only possible in the world of make-believe. Extinct species of plants and animals are lost to us forever.

a Write down the names of some other extinct animals.

How do we know extinct plants and animals ever existed?

When things die they usually decay to nothing, leaving no trace that they ever existed.
However, for a few plants and animals this is not the end of the story.

Where conditions are just right they become **fossils**.

b Under what conditions do fossils form?

Fossils provide scientists with information about plants and animals that occupied the Earth hundreds of millions of years before humans evolved.
Studying fossils helps scientists to understand how modern man and woman, i.e. Homo sapiens, **evolved**.

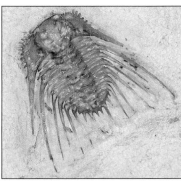

Fossilised Trilobite

Why do things become extinct?

Although fossils give us a record of the plants and animals that have become extinct, they don't tell us why these species eventually died out. Studying populations of plants and animals today gives us some clues as to why organisms became extinct all those millions of years ago.

Red panda at Edinburgh zoo

Here are some reasons why modern animal populations decrease.

▶ Animals are suited to a particular environment.
Change that environment and, unless they can adapt, their numbers will fall.

▶ Animals need to get enough of certain essential things like food.
If there isn't enough food, the number of animals will decrease.

▶ Some animals are valued by people and are hunted.

c Give some examples of animal populations that might be affected by hunting.

d Can you think of any other reasons why animal populations decrease?

e Can you suggest any reasons why plant populations decrease?

What are we doing to protect the species that remain?

When the population of a plant or animal starts to fall rapidly it becomes a **threatened species**. Once a population becomes so low that there is a real danger that the plant or animal may become extinct it becomes an **endangered species**.

f Find out the names of some plants or animals on the endangered species list.

g What can we do to ensure that the endangered species of today don't become the extinct species of tomorrow?

Zoos provide a safe haven for endangered animals. In **captive breeding programmes** endangered species are bred to increase the number of the species. One day, when conditions are favourable, it may be possible to reintroduce some of these animals back into the wild.

The **National Parks** in central and east Africa provide animals with the huge areas of land they need. This land has been put aside specifically for animals and plants and will not be developed for farming.

Institutions like the Royal **Botanical Gardens** in Edinburgh play an important role in cultivating plants that might otherwise have disappeared from the Earth. One day these might be reintroduced back into the wild.

When kept under suitable conditions, the seeds of many plants can be stored for many years in **seed banks**. Some time in the future the seeds can be used to reintroduce plants back into a suitable environment.

Serengetti National park

Royal Botanic Gardens, Edinburgh

Things to do

1 Copy and complete:
Many of the species of animals and plants that lived on the Earth millions of years ago have become . . . . We find the evidence that they existed in the form of . . . .

2 Make a list of some of the reasons why plant populations might decrease.

3 The dodo was a flightless birds found on the island of Mauritius. Trading ships used to call at the island for provisions on their long journeys around the world. These ships would carry animals like cats and rats that were not originally found on the island. Suggest why the dodo became extinct.

4 Scientists are not certain why dinosaurs became extinct but there are several interesting theories that attempt to explain their rapid disappearance from the Earth. Explore why dinosaurs became extinct using different reference sources such as the library and any websites you can find.

Fit for survival

Animals and plants have things about them that help them to survive in the place that they live.

▶ Look at the photographs.

Write down the things about each animal or plant that you think helps them to survive.

Oxford ragwort

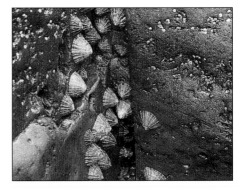

polar bear

flounder

mole

eyed hawk moth

The animals and plants in the photographs are **adapted** to living in particular habitats.
They have special **adaptations** that help them to survive.

▶ List some of the adaptations that help **you** to survive.

Survival is the name of the game

Here are 2 animals that are adapted to live in harsh environments.

▶ List the adaptations that you think each animal shows.
Then write down how each adaptation helps it to survive.

Mayfly larva

The mayfly larva lives in fast-flowing streams.

It clings tightly underneath rocks.

It has a flattened body with a very streamlined shape.

It feeds upon small plants growing on the rocks.

It has **gills** along the sides of its body and eyes on the top of its head.

It always moves away from the light into cracks between the stones.

Limpet

The limpet lives on the seashore.

It uses a sucker to cling tightly to rocks when the tide is out.

It has a thick shell to protect it from very high and very low temperatures.

It feeds on young seaweeds and it breathes using a gill to take in oxygen from the water.

Lice are nice!

Look carefully at your woodlice with a hand-lens.
Be careful not to damage them in any way.
How do you think they are adapted for living in leaf litter**?**

What conditions do you think woodlice like**?**
Make a list of your ideas (hypotheses).
You can use a **choice chamber** to find out if your ideas are right.

Plan an investigation to find out what conditions woodlice like.
Remember to make it a fair test.

- How many woodlice will you use**?**
- How will you record your results**?**

Show your plan to your teacher, then try it out.

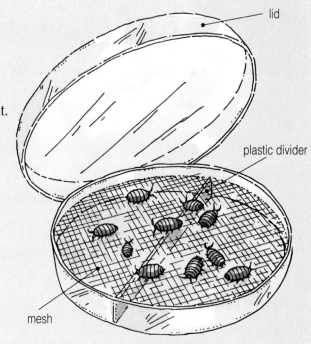

Choice chamber

---

1 How do you think that each of the following helps the animals to survive?
a) Deer and antelope are usually found together in herds.
b) Hoverflies have yellow stripes and look like wasps. But they are flies and have no sting.
c) Ragworms have good reflexes and can move back quickly into their burrows.

2 Suggest ways in which you think humans have been able to survive in the following environments:
a) hot desert   b) polar regions
c) highly populated cities.

3 Look at the numbers of eggs laid by these animals:

	Number of eggs
cod	3 million
frog	1000
snake	12
thrush	5

a) Why do you think the fish lays so many eggs?
b) Why does the snake lay far fewer eggs than the frog?
c) Why does a thrush lay so few eggs?

4 Look at these different bird beaks. Write down the name of each bird and say how you think its beak adapts it for survival.

Things to do

golden eagle   woodpecker   woodcock   mallard

Competition

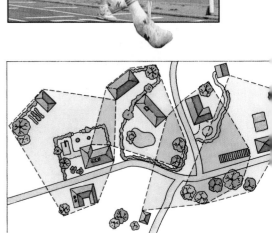

What does the word **competition** mean to you?

A race is a competition. Everyone tries very hard to win.
But there can only be one winner.

In nature, living things compete for **resources** that are in short
supply e.g. food and space.
Those that compete successfully will survive to breed.

▶ Write down some of the resources that animals compete for.

Write down some of the resources that plants compete for.

Seeing red

Robins compete for a **territory** (habitat) all the year round. They
sing to let other robins know that the territory is occupied. During
the breeding season they build a nest and raise their young inside
the territory. At this time they are very fierce and drive other robins
away.

a How many robin territories are shown on this map?

b What resources are the robins competing for?

c Why do you think that robins are so fierce to
other robins but not to all birds that
enter their territory?

Weed this!

A weed is a plant that is growing where it is not wanted e.g. poppies
in a wheat field.

It's easy to see why gardeners and farmers hate weeds and try hard
to get rid of them.

Weeds compete with the other plants for light, water and space.

The dandelion is a successful weed.
Can you see why?

▶ Look at the adaptations of the dandelion in the diagram.

Copy and complete the table:

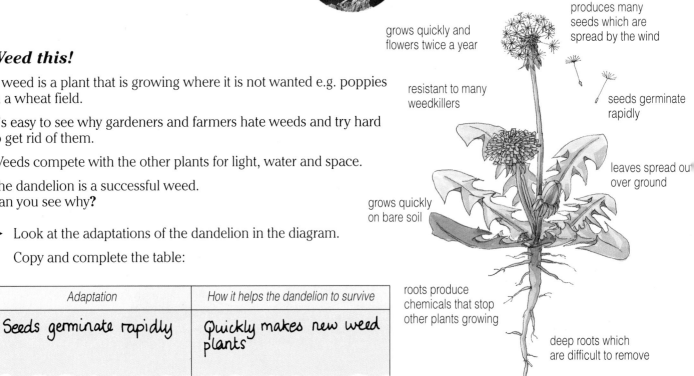

grows quickly and
flowers twice a year

produces many
seeds which are
spread by the wind

resistant to many
weedkillers

seeds germinate
rapidly

leaves spread out
over ground

grows quickly
on bare soil

roots produce
chemicals that stop
other plants growing

deep roots which
are difficult to remove

Adaptation	How it helps the dandelion to survive
Seeds germinate rapidly	Quickly makes new weed plants

Competition on the playing field

Dandelions, daisies and plantains compete with grass on your school field.

How could you find out which is the most successful weed?
You could count all of them, but this would take a very long time!
Instead you could take a **sample**. You could count the numbers of each weed in a small square called a **quadrat**.

1 Put your quadrat down on a typical area of the school field.
2 Count the numbers of dandelions, plantains and daisies inside your quadrat.
3 Take 4 more samples in different parts of the school field.
4 Record your results in a table like this:
- Add the totals of the class together for each weed.
- Draw a bar-chart of the class results.

d Why were you asked to take 5 samples?
e Which weed was the most successful on your school field?
f Try to think of a hypothesis that could explain this.
g What further investigation could you do to test this hypothesis?

Weed	Sample					
	1	2	3	4	5	Total
dandelions	3	3	4	0	2	12
plantains						
daisies						

Things to do

1 Copy and complete:
Living things . . . . for resources that are in . . . . supply, such as . . . . and . . . . Those plants and animals that . . . . successfully will . . . . to breed. Weeds compete with crops for . . . . and . . . .

2 Here are the planting instructions on a packet of broad bean seeds:
Sow the seeds about 5 cm deep and about 20 cm apart in open ground.
a) Why shouldn't the seeds be planted:
    i) any closer together? and
    ii) any further apart?
b) What resources might these plants compete for?

3 Can you think of any animals or plants that compete with humans?
Many of those that compete with us for food we call **pests**.
Write down any that you can think of and say what you think they compete with us for.

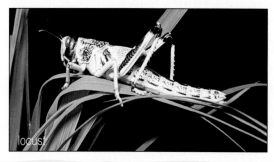

locust

A matter of life and death

18d

Predators are animals that kill other animals for food.

The animals that they kill are called **prey**.

▶ Make a list of 5 animals that you think are predators.

a Predators are usually bigger and fewer in number than their prey. Why do you think this is**?**

Look at the tiger:
It seems to have some unbeatable weapons.

▶ Think about the things that make it a good predator. Make a list.

Sometimes we think that predators have an easy time killing defenceless prey.
In fact the tiger has to work hard for its meal.
For every wild prey that it kills, the tiger fails 20–30 times.

b Predators often attack prey that is young, old, sick, weak or injured. Why do you think this is**?**

Tiger numbers have been threatened by hunting and by the destruction of their habitat.
A programme of **conservation** has given them more protection and their numbers are slowly increasing.

The predator strikes!

Choose one person to be the 'predator' in your group and blindfold him or her.

Arrange 9 discs at random on the squared paper.

Think of each disc as a prey animal.

Now the predator must search for the discs by tapping over the paper with one finger for one minute.

Each disc that the predator touches is removed. It counts as a 'kill'.

After each 'kill', the predator must pause and count to 3 before continuing.

After one minute count the total number of 'kills'.

Repeat the experiment, increasing the number of discs each time. Try 16, 25, 50 and 100 discs.

Record your results in a table.

Draw a graph of **number of kills** against **total number of prey**.

What are your conclusions from this activity**?**

Don't get caught!

▶ Look at the hare:

c How is it adapted to escape predators?

Here are some things that help prey to survive.

Explain how each one increases the chances of their survival.

d Run, swim or fly fast.
e Stay together in large numbers.
f Taste horrible.
g Have warning colours.

Life's ups and downs

The graph shows the number of lynx (predators) and the number of hares (prey) over a number of years.

Look at the graph carefully.

If the hares have plenty of food they breed and they increase in number (see ①).

This makes more food for the lynx, so their numbers increase (see ②).

▶ Answer these questions about what happens next:

h Why do the numbers of hares fall at ③?
i Why do the numbers of lynx fall at ④?
j Why do the numbers of hares increase at ⑤?
k Why are the numbers of prey usually greater than the numbers of predators?

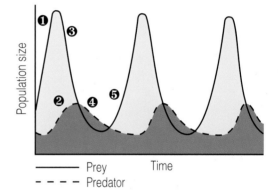

Prey ——
Predator – – – –

1 What do you think makes a good predator?
Make a picture of a make-believe predator that would catch lots of prey.

2 Some people think that predators are 'bad', but humans are the greatest predators that the world has known.
Write about some ways in which humans are predators.

3 Write about ways in which each of the following are successful predators:
a) domestic cat   b) spider   c) eagle.

4 The World Wildlife Fund started 'Operation Tiger'. This was a conservation programme aimed at protecting the tiger from extinction.
What do you think they did to protect the tigers?

Things to do

Population growth

A **population** is a group of the same animals or plants living in the same habitat e.g. greenfly on a rose bush or daisies in a lawn or a shoal of herring in the sea.

a Write down some more animal and plant populations and the habitats that they live in.

b Why do you think that animals and plants live together in populations?
Think about what they need for survival and how they keep up their numbers.

How do populations grow?

What happens if rabbits colonise a new area?
First there are a few of them and plenty of food.
Many will survive to breed and their numbers increase.
At first there are no predators to keep their numbers down.

Soon each generation is double the size of the previous one!
8 becomes 16, 32, 64, 128, 256, 512, and so on.
But this can only take place under ideal environmental conditions.

So why isn't the Earth over-run with rabbits?
The rabbit population can not go on increasing for ever, because not all of them will survive.
Some factors will start to *limit* the population growth, such as lack of food or being eaten by predators.

Here are some *limiting factors* that can slow down growth of populations:

- light   • overcrowding   • food and water   • disease
- climate   • predators   • oxygen   • shelter

▶ Copy and fill in the table for each factor above.

Factor	How the factor can limit population size
Light	lack of light slows growth of plants

People often think of populations as only being plants or animals.
But you can have populations of microbes too.
If you are ill you may have a population of bacteria or viruses inside your body!

The photo shows part of a yeast population:
For thousands of years, yeast has been used to change the sugar in barley into beer and the sugar in grapes into wine.
It also reacts with the sugar in dough to produce carbon dioxide.
This makes the dough rise to give us bread.

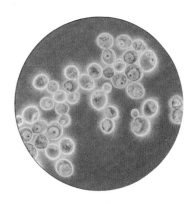

yeast cells

The growth of a yeast population

You can grow yeast cells in a sugar solution.

Add a suspension of yeast cells to the sugar solution in a conical flask.
Swirl the flask and plug its opening with cotton wool.
Place the flask in a warm cupboard or incubator at 20–25°C.

Over the next few days look at a drop of the yeast under a microscope.
Make sure that you use the same magnification each time.
Count the number of yeast cells that you can see and write it down.

After a while you may be able to draw a graph like the one here:

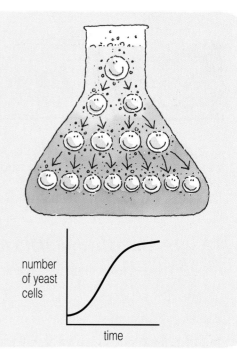

c What do you think happened to the number of yeast cells
   i) in the first few hours?   ii) later in the experiment?
   iii) at the end of the experiment?

d Why do you think the population of yeast cells stopped growing?

e What factors could you change in this experiment to increase or to decrease the growth rate of the yeast population?

Human effects

Humans can limit the growth of populations.
In many parts of the world large areas of forest are being cut down.
The trees are used for timber or the land is cleared for farming.

Trees should only be cut down if they can be replaced naturally or by planting. This would result in *sustainable* growth.

In a similar way fishermen are taking too many fish out of the sea.
Modern technology, such as the use of sonar to find the fish, more powerful ships and huge plastic nets, means more fish are caught.
Many species are *overfished* and in danger of extinction.

We should limit fishing so that enough fish survive and reproduce.

f What could be done to control the amount of fishing?

---

1 Copy and complete:
A . . . . is a group of animals or plants living in the same . . . . The growth of a . . . . can be limited by factors such as . . . . , ... and . . . . , so not all the young animals or plants in a population will . . . . to breed.

2 One of the slowest-breeding animals is the elephant. It has been worked out that, starting with one pair of elephants, their offspring would number 19 million after 700 years.
Explain why this could never actually happen.

3 Explain how you think each of the following would affect human population growth:
a) famine and disease
b) high birth rate
c) improved medical care.

Things to do

Evolution

Scientists estimate that there are between 20 and 30 million different species of plants and animals alive on the Earth today.
Where did such a huge variety of life come from**?**
One person who did more than any other to explain this was Charles Darwin.

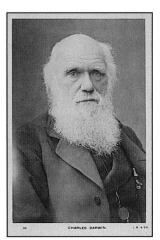

Charles Darwin

Charles Darwin and HMS Beagle

Charles Darwin lived in the nineteenth century. He was a keen naturalist and spent much of his time collecting plants and animals. In 1831 he sailed around the world on a small ship called *HMS Beagle*. The ship was going to gather information so that better maps could be made.

▶ Imagine that you are a naturalist like Darwin and that you have the opportunity to see and study the rare and unusual plants and animals that lived in far-off lands. What would you take on the journey**?** What sort of information might you gather**?**

The *Beagle* stopped in many different countries. The journey lasted for five years so Darwin had plenty of time to think about what he had seen.
He came to the conclusion that organisms **evolved** very slowly over many generations, and that this **evolution** was the result of **natural selection**.

Darwin suggested how evolution came about. He thought that, in every **generation**, small changes or **mutations** occur naturally in organisms. We now know that these mutations are small changes in genes. Most of the time, mutations have no effect on the lives of the organism. However, every now and again a really significant mutation occurs.

If a mutation helps an organism to survive, any organism that has it stands a better chance of surviving than organisms that doesn't have it. Over a long period of time the mutation would spread through the population. This is natural selection. Nature selects those organisms best suited to survive and rejects those organisms that are least suited.

Mountain hare in winter

▶ Mountain hares have white fur in the winter and brown fur in the summer. How do you think this makes them well suited to survival**?**

Mountain hare in summer

The Galapagos Islands

One of the places that *HMS Beagle* stopped on its journey was the Galapagos Islands.

▶ Find the Galapagos Islands in an atlas.
Look in the sea off the west coat of South America.

a Which country do the Galapagos Islands belong to?
b How many islands are there?
c Which is the biggest island?

▶ The word galápago means 'giant turtle' in Spanish.
It was used to describe the giant land tortoises that are found on the islands and gave the Islands its name.

The Galapagos Islands

What is special about these islands is that they were formed from volcanoes under the sea. At first, nothing lived on them. Later, they were colonised by organisms from the mainland.

d How might organisms have travelled the 900 km from the mainland to the islands?

The month that Darwin spent on the Galapagos Islands convinced him even more that his ideas about evolution were correct. He was sure that the organisms had evolved in different ways to those on the mainland because of the different conditions found on the islands.

The Galapagos Finches

Darwin was particularly interested in the Galapagos finches. He had seen similar finches on the South American mainland. They all had short straight beaks that they used to crush seeds. On the Galapagos, however, he was able to divide the 13 species of finches into six main groups. Each group had a beak specially adapted to eat a particular kind of food.

Your teacher will give you a sheet showing the heads of the different species of finch that live in the Galapagos Islands.

e What can you say about the shapes of the beaks?

f Can you suggest what the birds with short thick beaks feed on?

g Can you suggest what the birds with long thin beaks feed on?

Perhaps the most remarkable of all is the woodpecker finch. There are no true woodpeckers on the Galapagos but there are insects living in the trunks of trees.

A true woodpecker uses its long tongue to remove an insect from a hole but the woodpecker finch does not have a long tongue; instead it uses a cactus spine!

h How do you think a woodpecker finch is able to gather insects?

Woodpecker finch

When Darwin returned from his voyage on the *Beagle* he wrote about the ideas and evidence he had gathered in a book called '*The Origin of Species by means of Natural Selection*'. The reason why this book was so important was that it was the first theory of evolution to be fully supported by proper scientific evidence and an explanation of how it had happened.

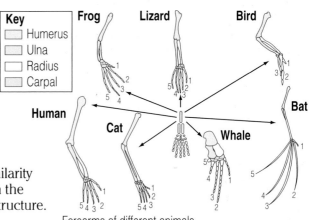
Forearms of different animals

Some evidence of evolution

One piece of evidence that supports Darwin's theory is the similarity in the structure of organisms. If different animals evolved from the same ancestor we ought to be able to see similarities in their structure. Look at the forearms of some different animals.

i In what ways are the forearms of the animals similar and in what ways are they different?

j Why did the forearms evolve in different ways?

---

1 Copy and complete:
Charles Darwin suggested that organisms . . . . as a result of . . . . Small changes or . . . . occurred to organisms from generation to generation. If these changes were favourable the organism would have a better chance of . . . . .

2 Shrews are active at night. They feed on insect sand worms and are themselves hunted by larger animals like owls and badgers. In terms of natural selection, discuss the possible effect of a mutation resulting in better night vision.

3 The ancestor of the modern giraffe had a much shorter neck.
a) What evidence do scientists have about the different stages in the evolution of the modern giraffe?
b) Describe how the modern giraffe has evolved by natural selection.

4 The French naturalist **Lamarck** proposed an alternative theory to explain why organisms evolve over many generations. This has become known as **Lamarckism**. Find out what you can about Lamarck and Lamarckism.

Things to do

Questions

1 A large herd of deer lived on an island.
The deer were sometimes killed by predators such as wolves.
To protect the deer population, some hunters shot all the wolves.
Then the deer population grew. Their numbers became so large
that they began to compete for grass. Many deer starved.
Soon the deer population was about the same as it was before the
wolves were shot.
a) What were the 4 populations involved?
b) Why do you think the hunters were wrong to shoot all the
   wolves?
c) What do you think will happen to the deer population in the
   future?

2 "Big, fierce animals are rare." Try to explain this statement.

3 Look at the way the leaves of these weeds are growing.
a) How do you think they survive trampling?
b) How do you think they affect the growth of the grass around
   them?
c) In what ways do gardeners cut down the competition from
   these weeds?

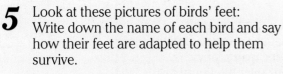

plantain   daisy   dandelion

4 Look at these samples of earthworm populations taken from 15 cm
under the soil:

Month	Jan.	Feb.	Mar.	Apr.	May	Jun.	Jul.	Aug.	Sep.	Oct.	Nov.	Dec.
number of worms	12	5	7	37	45	11	5	13	36	47	98	50
temperature (°C)	2	1	1	4	7	16	19	16	13	10	7	5
rainfall (mm)	40	30	25	50	80	20	5	25	40	50	80	70

a) Under what conditions do earthworms grow most successfully?
b) What do you think happens to the earthworms in hot weather?
c) Why do you think the earthworm numbers increase in the autumn?

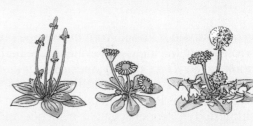

greenfinch

5 Look at these pictures of birds' feet:
Write down the name of each bird and say
how their feet are adapted to help them
survive.

mallard   woodpecker   osprey

Forces and motion

Everything that you do needs a force – a push or a pull.

You have already investigated forces, using a spring-balance to measure them (in newtons).
You found out about weight and friction. You measured the movement of toys.

In this topic you can use these ideas in new ways.

In this topic:
19a *Balanced forces*
19b *Bending and stretching*
19c *Moving at speed*
19d *Speed on graphs*

Balanced forces

Pushes and pulls are ***forces***.
The pictures show some forces, with their sizes
measured in ***newtons (N)***.

push = 50 N

100 N

weight = 1 newton

pull = 100 N

friction = 80 N

pull = 900 N   pull = 1000 N

upthrust of water = 400 N

weight = 400 N

a   Which is the biggest force shown in these diagrams**?**
b   Which is the smallest**?**
c   Which team is winning the tug-of-war**?** Which way is the
         rope moving**?** How do you know**?**
d   How can you tell that the woman is moving the crate**?**
         How big is the ***resultant*** force on the crate**?**

In two of the diagrams the forces are ***equal*** and ***opposite***.
We say they are **balanced** forces.

e   Which two diagrams show balanced forces**?**
f   How do you know that the girl is floating and not sinking**?**
g   What is the reading on the scale of the force-meter**?**
         What is the weight of a mass of 1 kilogram**?**

pull of spring = 10 N

1 kg

weight = 10 N

In each of the diagrams below, the forces are **balanced**.
Sketch or trace the drawings, and then for each one:
• label the size of the other force, in newtons,
• label the kind of force it is, choosing from:
    weight   **friction**   **upthrust**

h

weight = 20 N

j

hand pushing
iron = 10 N

i

Cornflakes

force of table on packet = 5 N

800 N
air resistance
(friction)

k

Sir Isaac Newton, 300 years ago, stated a scientific Law about balanced forces:
If the forces are balanced, the object   either   • stays still (like the cornflakes packet)
                                         or   • if it is moving, it continues to move at a
                                                   steady speed in a straight line (like the parachute).

Structures

Here are some photos of **structures**:

Sometimes you can see the structure.
For example, in a bridge or a crane, a fence or a tree, or a bicycle.

Sometimes the structure is hidden.
For example, the beams in the roof of your house, or the skeleton in your body.

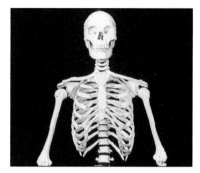

A structure can be designed by an engineer.
The structure must be strong enough to withstand the forces on it.
The forces in the structure must be *balanced* forces.

An engineering challenge!

Design and make a structure strong enough to support a 10 gram object as high as possible above the table.
You are given only:
- a 10 g object
- 20 straws
- 50 cm of sellotape. No more!

Your structure must be able to support the object for at least 30 seconds.
Try it!

- Who can build the tallest successful tower?

- Draw a labelled sketch of your tower.

- Look at the highest towers: how many triangles of straws can you count? Triangular shapes help to make a structure firm and rigid.

The straws you used are hollow tubes. A tube is stronger than a solid bar of the same weight. Why is a bike made from tubes?
Tubes are found in animals (e.g. a bird's bones) and in plants (e.g. the stem of a dandelion).

---

1 Copy and complete:
a) Pushes and pulls are . . . .
b) When the forces on an object are equal and opposite, we say they are . . . .
c) Sir . . . . Newton's first Law is: if the forces on an object are . . . . , then
- if the object is still, it stays . . . .
- if the object is moving, it continues to . . . . at a steady . . . . in a . . . . line.
d) Structures are usually stronger if they are built of . . . . shapes.
e) A tube is . . . . than a solid bar of the same weight.

2 List all the structures that you can see in the classroom (or your home).

3 List all the structures that you can see on the way home.

4 Explain, with a diagram, why a bicycle frame is a strong structure.

5 Use the things you have learned to design a very thin tall tower for a TV transmitter. Draw a labelled diagram.

Things to do

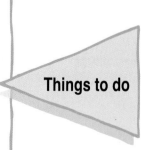

Bending and stretching

▶ Choose one of these 2 investigations, and do it.
If you have time, you can do the other one.

Bending beams

▶ Bridges need to be safe and strong.
Look at this photo of a beam bridge:

a Write down 3 materials that a beam bridge could be made from.

b Name 3 materials that you would not use to build a bridge.

A bridge is a structure. In the structure some parts are being squashed.
This is called **compression**. The tiny particles are pushed closer together.

➡COMPRESSION⬅

Other parts of the bridge are being stretched apart.
They are in **tension**.

⬅TENSION➡

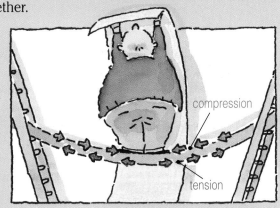

compression

tension

c What do you think is happening to the tiny particles
where the beam is in tension?

d Bend your ruler gently. Which part is being stretched?
Draw a diagram of your bent ruler and label the parts that
are in tension and the parts in compression.

Tara and her family are painting the ceiling:

Tara sees that the plank sags when her father stands on it.
It sags by a different amount when her baby sister stands on it.

• Write down what you think the sag of the plank depends on.
Give as much detail as you can. (This is your prediction.)
Try to include these words:

| *weight* | *tension* | *compression* | *balanced forces* |

• Plan an investigation to see if your prediction is true.
(You could use a ruler as the plank.)
How will you record your results?

• Show your plan to your teacher, and then do it.

• When you have finished, write your report.
Make sure you try to explain your results.

Stretching springs

Springs are useful in many ways:

- Make a list of all the uses of springs that you can think of.

You can make your own spring by winding copper wire round a pencil:

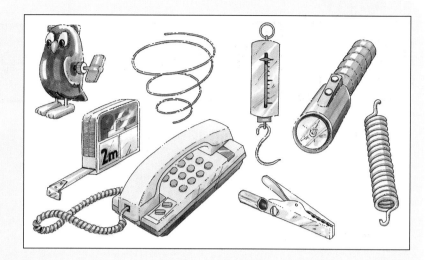

- Make a spring and then test it. Investigate how the length of your spring depends on the weight you hang on it.

- Plan your investigation carefully.
  How will you record your results?

- Check your plan with your teacher, and then do it. Start with small weights and carry on until your spring loses its shape.

- Plot a graph of the length (or, better, the stretch) of your spring against the weight hanging on it. What do you notice?

- If you have time, repeat your investigation with
  – a spring made from iron wire or nichrome wire, *or*
  – a piece of elastic or a rubber band.
  What differences do you find?

- Write a report of what you did and what you found out.

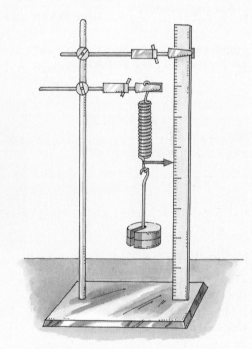

---

1 Peter likes to go fishing. He tested 2 new fishing lines by hanging weights on them. Here are his results:

weight (N)	0	5	10	15	20
length of line A (cm)	50	51	52	53	54
length of line B (cm)	50	52	54	56	58

a) What happens to the lines as he hangs weights on them?
b) How long is line A when the load weight is 20 N?
c) What is the load when line B is 52 cm?
d) Which of the lines was the more stretchy?
e) Both lines are made of nylon. Which do you think will be the stronger one?

2 Amy has long blonde hair and Ben has short black hair. Design an investigation to compare their hair strength.

3 Design a pram with springs so that it can travel over rough ground without shaking the baby.

4 Robert Hooke investigated springs over 300 years ago and wrote down Hooke's Law. Find out what is meant by Hooke's Law.

5 Use data shown in Question 1 to find the stretch ('extension') in each case. Plot 2 graphs (on the same axes). What do they show you?

Things to do

Moving at speed

Some things can move fast. Other things move slowly. They have a different **speed**.

Suppose the horse in the picture has a constant speed of 10 metres per second.
This means that it travels 10 metres in every second.

The speed can be found by:

Travelling at 10 m/s

Average speed = $\dfrac{\textbf{distance travelled} \text{ (in metres)}}{\textbf{time taken} \text{ (in seconds)}}$

Speed can also be measured in miles per hour (m.p.h.) or kilometres per hour (km/h).

Example
In a race, this girl runs 100 metres in 20 seconds.
What is her average speed?

Answer
$$\text{Average speed} = \frac{\text{distance travelled}}{\text{time taken}}$$

$$= \frac{100 \text{ metres}}{20 \text{ seconds}}$$

$$= 5 \text{ m/s}$$

(This is about 10 m.p.h.)

This is her **average** speed because she may speed up or slow down during the race.
If she speeds up, she is **accelerating**. If she slows down, she is **decelerating**.

▶ Copy out this table, and then complete it.

	Distance travelled	Time taken	Average speed
a	20 m	2 s	
b	100 m	5 s	
c	2 m		1 m/s
d		10 s	50 m/s
e	2000 km	2 h	

▶ Now match the speeds in the table with these objects. Which is which?
Add the names to the first column of your table.

Safety matters

When a driver has to brake, it takes time for him to react.
In that fraction of a second, the car can travel many metres.
This is called the **thinking distance**.

For most people, when they are not expecting to brake, the reaction time is 0.7 second!

No seat belts! Testing cars with dummies

f Suppose you were driving at 20 m/s (this is 45 mph).
If your reaction time is 0.7 s, how far would you travel before you started to press the brake?

g How would this thinking distance be affected if the driver was tired?
What else could affect this thinking distance?

▶ The **braking distance** is the distance the car will travel **after** the brake is pressed.

h At 20 m/s (45 mph) on a dry road, with good brakes, the braking distance is 31 m.
What is the **total stopping distance**?

i On a wet road, the braking distance is **twice** as much. **Why** is it longer?
What is the total stopping distance then?

j What other things would affect the braking distance?

Shortest stopping distances, *on a dry road, with good brakes*

At 13 m/s (*30 mph*)

Thinking distance	Braking distance	Total stopping distance
9 m	14 m	23 m

At 22 m/s (*50 mph*)

Thinking distance	Braking distance	Total stopping distance
15 m	38 m	53 m

At 30 m/s (*70 mph*)

Thinking distance	Braking distance	Total stopping distance
21 m	75 m	96 m

The distances shown in car lengths are based on an average family car.

---

1 Copy and complete:
a) The formula for speed is:
b) The units for speed are m/s (. . . . per . . . .) or km/h (. . . . per . . . .) or m.p.h. (. . . . per . . . .).
c) If a car speeds up it is . . . .
If a car slows down it is . . . .
d) The thinking distance is . . . .
The braking distance is . . . .

2 A girl jogs at 2 m/s.
a) How far would she go in 10 seconds?
b) How long would she take to go 400 m?

3 Copy and complete this table:

Name of runner	Distance (metres)	Time taken (seconds)	Speed (m/s)
Ayesha	60	10	
Ben		5	8
Chris	100		5
Donna	400		4

4 Suppose a driver can see only 25 m because it is misty. What should his maximum speed be?

Things to do

Speed on graphs

Tanni Grey-Thompson winning a Gold Medal at the Paralympic Games

a The athlete in the photo can travel 70 metres in 10 seconds. What is her average speed?

b What does average mean? Does it mean she travelled at exactly this speed for all 10 seconds?

To see how speed varies during a journey, it helps to draw a graph.
It can show you where you speed up or slow down.
There are 2 kinds of graph you can use.

1. Distance – time graph

Imagine going on a bicycle ride.
The graph shows a bike ride with 3 parts, labelled **A**, **B**, **C**.
Look at the labels on the 2 axes:

Part **A**.
The cyclist is travelling at *a steady speed*.
As **time** passes (along the graph), the **distance** increases (up the graph).

Part **B**.
The cyclist has *stopped* for a rest.
As time passes (along the graph), the distance stays the same.

Part **C**.
The cyclist is now travelling again, and is going *faster* than before.
The graph is *steeper*, because she is travelling a bigger distance in each second.
The faster the speed, the steeper the slope or **gradient**.

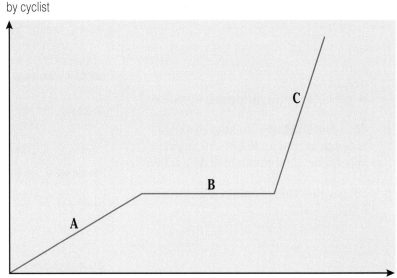

distance travelled by cyclist

time taken

A
a steady speed (slow)

B
stopped for a rest

C
travelling faster

c How would the graph be different if she had stayed for a longer rest in part B?

d How would it be different if she had moved even faster in part C?

e Calum makes a journey on his bike.
Sketch a graph that shows his journey:
He sets off from home, riding slowly for 1 minute.
Then he stops at the traffic lights for 1 minute.
He sets off again, riding at exactly the same speed as before, for 2 minutes. Then he stops for a rest for 1 minute.
Finally he rides very quickly down a hill for 1 minute.

2. Speed – time graph

This graph shows the **speed**–time graph for a **car journey**.
The graph has 4 parts, labelled **P**, **Q**, **R**, **S**.
Look at the labels on the axes:

Part **P**.
Here the car is speeding up (***accelerating***).
As time passes (along the graph),
the speed increases (up the graph).

Part **Q**.
It is travelling at a ***constant speed*** of 10 m/s.

Part **R**.
The car ***accelerates*** to travel at a higher speed.

Part **S**.
The speed of the car drops very quickly to
zero. Perhaps it has crashed into a wall!

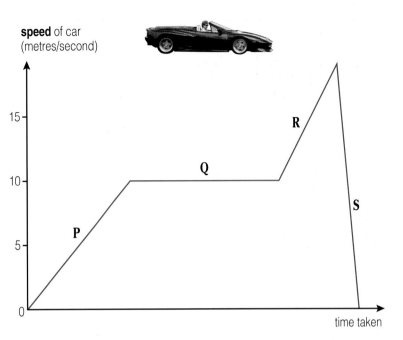

f Jack starts his car, accelerates to 10 m/s, keeps at this
speed for a while and then brakes quickly to a stop.
Sketch the speed–time graph for his journey.

Here is a speed–time graph for a **sky-diver** who
jumps out of an aeroplane:

g At which point (A, B, C, D, E) did he jump?

h In which part does he speed up (accelerate)
due to the pull of gravity (his weight)?

i After a while, the air resistance balances
his weight, and so he stops going any faster.
What is his speed now?

j Which point shows his parachute opening?

k What is his speed with the parachute open?

l Why is he slower than before?

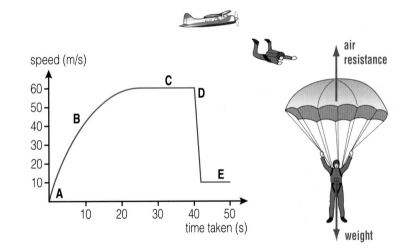

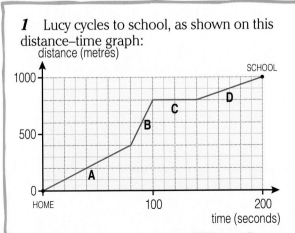

1 Lucy cycles to school, as shown on this
distance–time graph:

a) Which parts show that Lucy is moving?
b) For how long did she stop at some
traffic lights?
c) Which part is most likely to show her
going down a hill? Explain why.
d) How far did she travel during part A?
e) Calculate her speed during part A.
f) Calculate her speed during part B.
g) How far is it from home to school?
h) Calculate her average speed for the
whole journey.

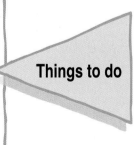

Things to do

2 Explain what is meant by ***gradient***.

Questions

1 Your weight is the force of gravity pulling you down.
On Earth, a mass of 1 kilogram weighs 10 newtons.

a) In what units do we measure: i) mass? ii) weight?
b) What is your: i) mass? ii) weight?
c) When you are standing on the ground there are 2 balanced forces acting on you – your weight, and the ground pushing up on your shoes. Draw a labelled diagram of this.
d) The table shows the gravitational pull near different bodies in the Solar System:
   i) Can you see any pattern between size and gravitational pull?
   ii) What would be your weight on the Moon?
   iii) On which planet would you weigh most, and least?
e) Imagine that you lived on the Moon where gravity is only about one sixth that of Earth. What difference would this make to the way in which things move?

Body	Gravity compared to the Earth
Sun	27.96
Mercury	0.38
Venus	0.90
Earth	1.00
Moon	0.17
Mars	0.38
Jupiter	2.54
Saturn	1.07
Uranus	0.90
Neptune	1.20
Pluto	0.05

2 Judy tested a spring by hanging weights on it.
Here are her results:
a) Plot a line-graph of her results.
b) Write a sentence to say what conclusion you can draw from this graph.

weight (N)	1	2	3	4	5	6
extension (mm)	15	30	45	60	80	120

3 Holly the cat goes for a little walk.
Here is her distance–time graph:

a) Use the scales on the graph to describe her journey in as much detail as you can.
b) What is her speed in part A?
c) Sketch the graph you would get if she runs twice as fast in parts A and C.
Add the correct numbers to your axes.

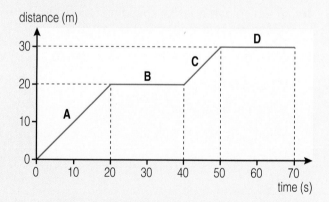

4 The data in the table is from the Highway Code.
It shows the shortest stopping distances for a car at different speeds on a dry road. Look at the table carefully.
a) What do you think is meant by 'Thinking distance'?
b) How would it change if the driver had been drinking alcohol?
c) What do you think is meant by 'Braking distance'?
d) How would it change if the road was icy?
e), f), g) What are the missing numbers in the table?
h) What figures should be in the last row of the table?

Speed of car	Thinking distance (feet)	Braking distance (feet)	Overall stopping distance (feet)
20 mph	20	20	40
30 mph	(e)	45	75
40 mph	40	(f)	120
50 mph	50	125	(g)
60 mph			

Atoms, elements and compounds

Atoms are the building blocks from which everything is made. An atom is the smallest part of an element. There are 92 naturally occurring elements. How many can you name? Elements combine together in chemical reactions to form compounds.

In this topic you will learn about the structure of an atom. You will also be looking at lots of elements and some of the compounds formed from them.

The mighty atom

Atoms are the building blocks from which all things are made.

An atom is the smallest particle of a substance that can take part in a chemical reaction.

The word **atom** comes from a Greek word that means 'something that cannot be cut'.

Dalton's Atomic Theory

John Dalton was a chemist who spent much of his working life in Manchester. In 1808, as a result of his own experiments and those of others, he made some suggestions about the nature of atoms.

Dalton suggested that:

1. Chemical elements are made up of very small particles called atoms.
2. Atoms cannot be created or destroyed.
3. All atoms of the same element are identical but different to atoms of any other element.
4. When atoms combine to form compounds, they do so in simple fixed whole numbers.

Which two of these statements still hold true today**?**

Which two of these statements were subsequently found to be incorrect**?**

Dalton devised a set of atomic symbols that he used to represent atoms and compounds:

These symbols represent copper oxide:

Which gases are represented by these symbols?

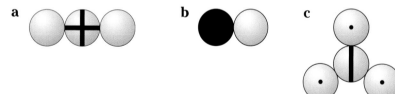

John Dalton

ELEMENTS

Dalton's table of elements

Models of the atom

Dalton's atomic theory accounted for many but not all of the observations made by scientists.

Towards the end of the nineteenth century scientists began to wonder if an atom really was an indivisible particle or was an atom itself made up of even smaller **subatomic particles?**

In 1897, the physicist **J. J. Thomson** discovered the **electron**. He proposed that an atom was actually composed of a solid sphere of positive charge with negative electrons stuck in it rather like plums in a plum pudding. This became known as the **plum pudding** model of the atom.

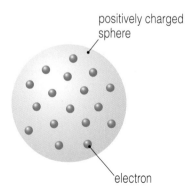

positively charged sphere

electron

Plum pudding model of the atom

A different atomic structure was proposed by **Rutherford** in 1911. As a result of some research carried out by his students Marsden and Geiger, Rutherford concluded that most of the mass of an atom is found at its centre, or **nucleus**. He said that this nucleus carries positive charge. We now know that this is due to the presence of positively charged particles called **protons**. He also concluded that electrons are not found in the nucleus but around it.

Rutherford predicted the existence of particles in the nucleus that carry no charge. Chadwick proved the existence of these neutral particles, called **neutrons**, in 1932.

The final piece of the great atomic puzzle was provided by the Dane, **Niels Bohr**, in 1914. He showed that the electrons around the nucleus of an atom were to be found in definite shells or orbitals at different distances from the nucleus. In some ways they were like the planets in the Solar System orbiting around the Sun.

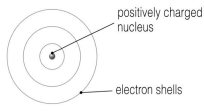

Rutherford's model of the atom

The Bohr atom

Atomic structure

Atoms are made of three subatomic particles called electrons, neutrons and protons.

The electron is much lighter than the proton or neutron and is usually given a mass of zero although, in reality, its mass is about 0.0005 atomic mass units.

An atom consists of a nucleus of protons and neutrons surrounded by shells of electrons.

The atomic number of an element is the number of protons in each atom. This is the same as the number of electrons because atoms are neutral.

d What is the atomic number of the atom opposite?

In the next lesson you will be looking in detail at the pattern of elements in the Periodic Table.

e Look up the atomic numbers of some elements in the Periodic Table. What do you notice about how elements are arranged?

Particle	Mass in atomic mass units	Charge carried
Electron	0	− ve
Neutron	1	none
Proton	1	+ ve

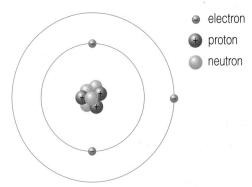

Structure of an atom of lithium

Things to do

1 Copy and complete:
a) The nucleus of an atom carries a .... charge.
b) Electrons carry a .... charge.
c) The nucleus of an atom contains positively charged particles called ....
d) The particles in the nucleus that carry no charge are called .....
e) An atom consists of a nucleus containing .... and .... surrounded by shells of ....

2 Which of the following statements is true and which of them is false?
a) Most of the mass of an atom is found in its nucleus.
b) Protons and electrons carry the same charge.
c) Electrons are found in the nucleus of an atom.
d) Neutrons and protons have the same mass.

3 a) Use Dalton's atomic symbols to represent the following chemical compounds:
    i)   Water (H_2O).
    ii) Carbon dioxide (CO_2).
    iii) Copper sulphate ($CuSO_4$).
b) The atomic symbols we use today are very different to those used by Dalton. Suggest why this is.

The Periodic Table

What do you remember about **elements?**

Elements are substances which *cannot be broken down into anything simpler*.
An element has *only one type of atom*.

You've met lots of elements already.
Which of the elements in the box:

a rusts**?**
b has the symbol H**?**
c has the symbol S**?**
d has the symbol Cu**?**
e turns blue with starch**?**
f is about 21% of the air**?**

Elements
copper
iron
hydrogen
iodine
oxygen
sulphur

g What does *classifying* mean**?**

Scientists classify the elements in the **Periodic Table**.
But how are the elements arranged**?**
Let's look for patterns.

The elements here are sodium, gold, copper and chlorine. Can you identify each one**?**

How are books classified in your school library**?**

Grouping elements

Look at this information about elements.

Element	Melting point in °C	Boiling point in °C	Appearance	Reaction with cold water	Other information
sodium	98	890	silver-grey solid	reacts violently	conducts heat and electricity
silver	960	2212	shiny silver solid	no reaction	conducts heat and electricity
helium	−270	−269	colourless gas	no reaction	very unreactive, doesn't conduct
lithium	181	1330	silver-grey solid	reacts very quickly	conducts heat and electricity
copper	1083	2595	shiny pink-brown solid	no reaction	conducts heat and electricity
chlorine	−101	−34	green-yellow gas	dissolves	reactive, doesn't conduct
argon	−189	−186	colourless gas	no reaction	very unreactive, doesn't conduct
fluorine	−220	−188	pale yellow gas	dissolves	very reactive, doesn't conduct
gold	1063	2966	shiny gold solid	no reaction	conducts heat and electricity
potassium	63	765	silver-grey solid	reacts very violently	conducts heat and electricity
neon	−250	−246	colourless gas	no reaction	very unreactive, doesn't conduct
bromine	−7	58	red-brown liquid	dissolves	reactive, doesn't conduct

Make a data card for each element.
Use your cards to match up similar elements.
You can move the cards around to get the best match.

● Which elements have you grouped together**?** Why**?**
● Within each of your groups, put the elements in order.
● Explain your order.

DATA CARD
Element ___
Appearance ___
Melting point ___
Boiling point ___
Reactivity ___

Mendeleev was a Russian scientist. In 1869 he made
a pattern of elements. He put the elements in **groups**.
This pattern is called the **Periodic Table**.

Your teacher will show you a copy of the **Periodic Table**.
The columns of elements are called **groups**.
The rows of elements are called **periods**.
Are *your* groups the same as those in the Periodic Table?

h   Which elements are in the same group as chlorine?

i   Name 2 elements in the same period as chlorine.

j   Where are the *metals* in the Periodic Table?

k   Within each group, where are the *most reactive* metals?

Your teacher may show you some metals reacting.
How do sodium and magnesium react with water?

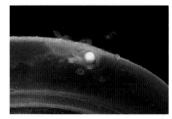   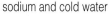   

sodium and cold water   magnesium and cold water   magnesium and steam

l   Which is more reactive, sodium or magnesium?

▶   Look at a copy of the full Periodic Table.

m   Write the symbol and name of the most reactive metal.
        (You can use your answers to **j**, **k** and **l**, to help you answer this.)

Video highlights

The Spotlight Video Company needs your help.
The company wants to make a new video.
It will be about elements and the Periodic Table.

- The video will be for 13-year-old pupils.
- It should be about 5 minutes long.
- It should be interesting and exciting. (It *might* be funny!)
- It should explain about elements and the Periodic Table.

Your group should write a script for the video.
What will be seen on the screen? Explain what filming will be
needed.
Who would you like to present your video? Money is no object!

1   Copy and complete:
a)   Elements have only one type of . . . .
b)   Elements are classified in the . . . . Table.
c)   The columns of elements are called . . . .
d)   The rows of elements are called . . . .

2   Name 2 elements in each case which
are: a) solids   b) liquids   c) gases.

3   Choose one group of elements.
Use books to find out about the group.
Make a wall poster about the elements.

Things to do

Two's company

Legoland

Lego can make lots of different things.
The pieces are building blocks.

A few **elements** can make lots of **compounds**.
The elements are the building blocks.

> Elements have only one type of atom.
> Compounds have two or more different atoms joined together.

a Which boxes contain the elements?

1	2	3	4	5

▶ Here are some formulas for compounds. See if you can work out their names.

b MgO   **d** HCl   **f** CO_2

c $CuCl_2$ **e** FeS   **g** H_2O

Some common compounds

▶ Look around the room.

h Write down some of the compounds you can see.

i Write down some of the elements you can see.

Most elements are not found on their own. They are in compounds.

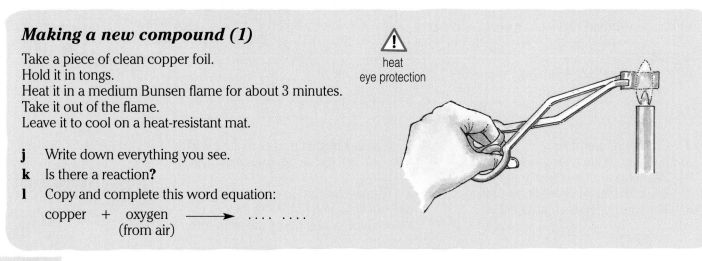

Making a new compound (1)

Take a piece of clean copper foil.
Hold it in tongs.
Heat it in a medium Bunsen flame for about 3 minutes.
Take it out of the flame.
Leave it to cool on a heat-resistant mat.

⚠️ heat
eye protection

j Write down everything you see.

k Is there a reaction?

l Copy and complete this word equation:

copper + oxygen ⟶ ....
(from air)

Making a new compound (2)

Follow the instructions opposite to make a new compound:

m Write down everything you see.

n How do you know there is a reaction?

The symbol equation is:
$CuO + H_2SO_4 \longrightarrow CuSO_4 + H_2O$

o Copy and complete the word equation:
. . . . + sulphuric acid $\longrightarrow$ copper sulphate + ...

Half fill a test-tube with dilute sulphuric acid.
Add one spatula measure of copper oxide.
Stir the liquid.
Leave the tube in your
rack for 5 minutes.

⚠
acid
eye protection

Making a new compound (3)

Follow the instructions opposite to make a new compound:

p Write down everything you see.

q How do you know there is a reaction?

r Copy and complete the word equation:
. . . . + copper sulphate $\longrightarrow$ zinc sulphate + ...

s Copy and complete the symbol equation:
$Zn + ... \longrightarrow ZnSO_4 + ...$

t Do you think copper will react with zinc sulphate?
Explain your answer. Test out your prediction.

Half fill a test-tube with copper sulphate solution.
Put a piece of zinc into the tube.
Stir the liquid.
Leave the tube in your
rack for 5 minutes.

⚠
eye protection

Breaking compounds

When elements join together they make compounds.
It is not easy to get the elements back.

Look at this sample of copper sulphate crystals:
Copper sulphate has the formula $CuSO_4$.
It contains copper, sulphur and oxygen. How could you get the
copper out? Discuss this in your group. Write down your ideas.
Your teacher may let you try some of them.

---

1 Copy and complete:
a) . . . . have only one type of atom.
b) . . . . have 2 or more different atoms
joined together.
c) Magnesium can react with oxygen in the
air. The word equation is:
. . . . + ... $\longrightarrow$ . . . .
d) The formula of . . . . is MgO.

2 Draw a table like this:

Element	Compound

Put these in the correct column:
chlorine   glass   gold
sugar   iron oxide   sulphur
carbon   copper sulphate

3 Look at Ann's science homework.

> I lit a spill. I put it into a tube
> of hydrogen gas. The gas
> reacted with oxygen in the air.
> I saw a flash. I heard a 'pop'
> sound. I made some water
> in the tube.

From Ann's work:
a) Write the names of 2 elements.
b) Write the name of 1 compound.
c) Was there a reaction?
How do you know?
d) Write a word equation.

Things to do

49

20d It's a fix

▶ Look at each statement below.
Is it a description of an element? Is it possible to tell?
Write down your ideas. Use a code for each answer: ✓ for *element*
? for *not possible to tell*
✗ for *non-element*.

a   made of only one type of atom
b   is called water
c   looks shiny
d   made of atoms
e   gives off carbon dioxide when heated

f   made of molecules
g   has the symbol Sn
h   has the symbol O_2
i   has the formula CO
j   has the formula FeS

▶ Discuss the ideas with others in your group. Do you all agree?

Researching compounds

Use books or ROMs to find out which elements make up these compounds:

k   PVC   l   paper 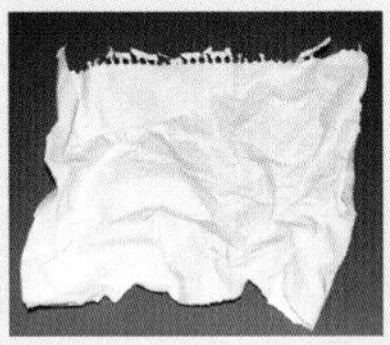   m   candle wax    n   Teflon

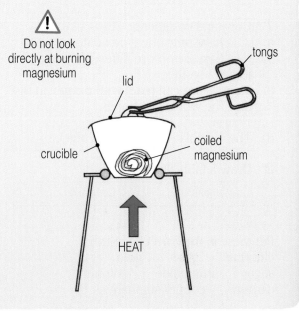

How much of each?

Compounds are made when elements join together.
But **how much** of each element?

Magnesium reacts with oxygen in the air.
But how much of each reacts?

Look at the diagram. This apparatus could help you find out.

magnesium + oxygen ⟶ magnesium oxide

In this experiment you need to know how much magnesium you start with. You then need to know how much magnesium oxide you make.
How do you think you can do this using the apparatus drawn?
Discuss this in your group.

Your teacher will give you an instruction sheet.
Read through all the instructions before you start.
This is a difficult experiment. Your results will tell your teacher how well you have done it!

⚠ Do not look directly at burning magnesium

tongs
lid
coiled magnesium
crucible
HEAT

How much of each? – The results

Each group should have a result. Your teacher will collect these from all the groups.
Copy the class results into a table like this one:

Group	Mass of magnesium at start in grams	Mass of magnesium oxide at end in grams
A		
B		
C		
D		

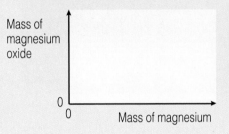

Draw a graph of the results.

Mass of magnesium oxide

0

0   Mass of magnesium

What do you notice? Can you see a pattern in your results?

Magnesium reacts with oxygen. The masses of each element which combine are in **proportion**.
A fixed amount of magnesium always combines with a fixed amount of oxygen. The compound has **fixed composition**.
The compound always has the formula MgO.

▶ Copy and complete the table. The first one has been done for you.

Name	Formula	Number of each type of atom
aluminium chloride	AlCl$_3$	1 aluminium 3 chlorine
magnesium oxide	MgO	
sodium fluoride	NaF	
	Al$_2$O$_3$	
	H$_2$O	
		1 carbon 4 chlorine

Things to do

1 Copy and complete:
Compounds have . . . . composition. They have a fixed formula. The . . . . for carbon dioxide is CO$_2$. It has . . . . carbon atom and . . . . oxygen atoms.

2 Draw a room where you live. You can draw people and furniture in your room. Label 10 objects in the room. Say what they are made from. Say whether they are elements or compounds.

3 Luke made a graph of some class results.

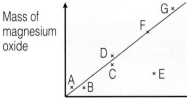

a) Which group had a strange result? What do you think went wrong?
b) Which 2 groups started with the same amount of magnesium?

Chemistry at Work

Elements and compounds

Sulphur

Sulphur is used in the first step in making
sulphuric acid. Molten sulphur is sprayed
into a furnace and burned in a blast of hot air.

a   Which gas in the air does the sulphur react with**?**

b   Write a word equation to show what happens
       when sulphur burns in air.

c   Why do the gases given off from a factory making
       sulphuric acid have to be carefully monitored**?**

Look at the table below showing the uses of
sulphuric acid:

Uses of sulphuric acid	Percentage used (%)
Making new chemicals	25.7
Paints and pigments	21.6
Detergents and soaps	13.3
Fertilisers	11.2
Plastics	7.0
Fibres	5.3
Dyes	2.8
Other uses	

d   Work out the percentage of sulphuric acid that should
       be under the heading 'Other uses' in the table above.

e   Use a computer to display the uses of sulphuric acid
       in a pie-chart.

Magnesium

Magnesium is used in fireworks and flares.

f   What is the colour of the flame produced
       when magnesium burns**?**

g   Write a word equation for magnesium burning.

h   The makers of fireworks want magnesium to burn
       more quickly than a piece of magnesium ribbon.
       What can they do to the magnesium to make this
       happen**?**

Mixtures

Helium and oxygen

Did you know that helium is used by deep-sea divers? It is mixed with oxygen gas for divers to breathe in. This is safer than breathing in normal air which contains nitrogen. The nitrogen can dissolve in a diver's blood and can form a bubble as the diver rises to the surface. This can kill the diver.

i Which gas do you think is more soluble in blood, nitrogen or helium? Why do you think this?

j What do divers call it when a bubble of gas is formed in their circulatory system?

k What happens to the voice of a diver breathing in a mixture of oxygen and helium?

l Find out about and explain another use of helium.

Alloys

An alloy is a ***mixture of metals***.
Alloys are made to improve the properties of a metal. For example, steel is an alloy of iron.
It has traces of carbon mixed with the iron, but can also have other metals added.
Tungsten mixed in makes the steel very hard and is used to make cutting tools.
Cobalt and nickel are added to make stainless steel, which does not rust.

m Which type of steel would you use to make the sharp edge of a lathe tool in your technology department?

n Name some objects that are made from stainless steel.

o Why aren't cars made from stainless steel?

p The atoms of a pure metal are all the same size and packed closely together in layers.
Explain why adding atoms of a different size might make it more difficult to bend the metal.

q Find out about the alloys used to make aeroplanes or the alloys used to make coins.

Questions

1

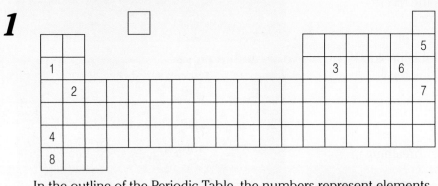

In the outline of the Periodic Table, the numbers represent elements.
Give the **numbers** of:
a) 3 elements in the same period
b) 3 elements in the same group
c) 2 metals with similar properties
d) 2 non-metals with similar properties
e) the most reactive metal.

Sodium   Potassium   Lithium

2 Name an element in each case which:
a) is a gas at room temperature and made of molecules
b) is always present in sulphides
c) is a non-metal and a liquid at room temperature
d) has the symbol N
e) is a more reactive metal than sodium
f) is present in all the molecules opposite.

methane CH_4
sugar $C_6H_{12}O_6$
carbon dioxide CO_2
propane C_3H_8
ethanol C_2H_5OH

3 State an important use of each of the elements:
a) sulphur
b) magnesium
c) helium
d) copper
e) iron

4 Copy and complete these word equations:
a) magnesium + sulphur $\longrightarrow$ _____ _____
b) zinc + iron sulphate $\longrightarrow$ _____ _____ + _____
c) magnesium + _____ oxide $\longrightarrow$ _____ _____ + copper
d) zinc oxide + sulphuric acid $\longrightarrow$ _____ _____ + water

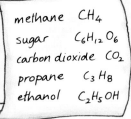

Can you write symbol equations too?

5 a) Name the compound made when iron reacts with chlorine.
b) Give 2 differences between iron metal and compounds containing iron.
c) Which is more reactive, iron or magnesium?
   Write about 2 experiments you could do to find out.
   What apparatus would you use?
   What measurements would you make?
   What results would you expect?

6 What is an alloy? Give the names of some alloys and say what they are used for.

Energy

21

Without energy nothing can ever happen!

All living things need energy to stay alive and to move.
You get your energy from food.

Our homes, transport and factories need the energy that
comes from fuels.
But the world is running out of fuel . . . .

Go with energy

a Name 4 things in your home that use electricity.

b Why do we need to eat food?

c Make a list of 5 things that you have done today. Put them in order, starting with the one that you think needs most energy.

If you climb to the top of a ladder, you have more gravitational **potential** energy.
An object which is moving has **kinetic** energy.

d Complete this sentence:
When a skier is moving downhill, ... energy is transferred to .... energy.

▶ Look at the diagram. It shows an electric motor lifting up a weight:

e What kind of energy does the moving wheel have?

f Where does this energy come from?

g Copy and complete its **Energy Diagram**:

h From the diagram, what can you say about the amount of energy (in joules) **before** the transfer and **after** the transfer?

i How much of the energy after the transfer is useful? What has happened to the rest?

We say its **efficiency** is 70%, because only 7 out of 10 joules have done something useful.

This is what usually happens in energy transfers. Although there is the same amount of energy afterwards, not all of it is useful.

▶ Now look at this diagram:

j What happens to the lamp? Why?

k Suppose the weight starts with 100 J of potential energy, and then 20 joules appear as light energy shining from the lamp. What has happened to the other 80 joules?

l What is the efficiency of the lamp in this case?

m Draw an Energy Diagram for this, and then label it.

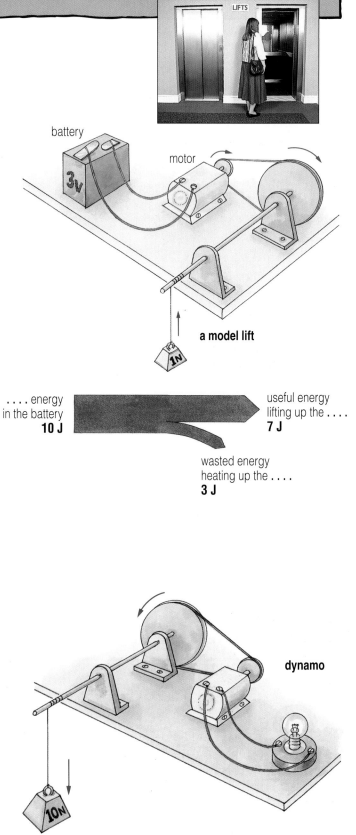

a model lift

.... energy in the battery
10 J

useful energy lifting up the ....
7 J

wasted energy heating up the ....
3 J

dynamo

Energy transfers

Your teacher will show you some of these.
Observe them carefully, and think about the energy transfers.
For each one, draw an Energy Diagram and label it.

n   an electric kettle

o   a clockwork toy

p   a solar-powered calculator

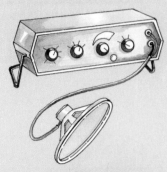

q   a signal-generator and loudspeaker

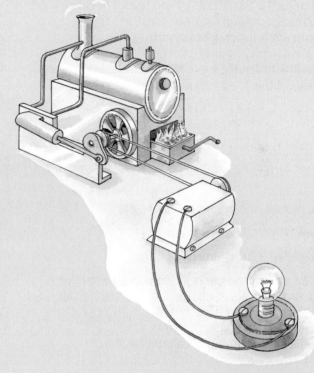

s   a steam engine and dynamo

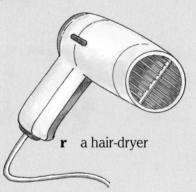

r   a hair-dryer

---

1 Copy and complete:
a) Energy is measured in . . . .
b) Lifting a stone gives it . . . . energy.
c) A moving object has . . . . energy.
d) In any energy transfer, the total amount of . . . . before the transfer is always . . . . to the total amount of . . . . afterwards.
e) After the transfer, not all of the . . . . is useful.

2 Describe the energy transfers involved in:
a) a torch,
b) a TV set,
c) playing a guitar.

3 What happens if the food you eat contains more energy than you need?

4 Petrol (chemical energy) is put in a car. Give examples from different parts of the car of the forms that energy can be changed to.

5 Are some kettles cheaper to run than others? Plan an investigation to compare some kettles.
How will you make it a fair test?

6 Why do you think it is impossible for anyone to build a perpetual-motion machine?

Things to do

21b   *Energy from the Sun*

a   Where does the Earth get most of its energy from**?**
b   Think of all the things that happen because of the Sun.
Make a list of as many as you can.

Making food

Green plants can capture the energy in the sunlight.
The green chemical in their leaves is called **chlorophyll**.
It *absorbs* the Sun's energy and uses it to make food.
It also makes oxygen for us to breathe.
This process is called **photosynthesis**.

Because plants make food, they are called producers.
Animals eat this food – they are consumers.

In this picture, the energy transfers are:

Sun ➡ vegetables ➡ human

This is called a **food-energy chain**.

Here are some food-energy chains that are in the
wrong order. Write each one in the correct order.
c   rabbit, Sun, grass, fox
d   humans, grass, sheep, Sun
e   thrush, Sun, cabbage, caterpillar

Biofuel

Plant and animal materials are called **biomass**.
As well as being food, biomass can give us energy in other ways:

- Wood is a fuel. It can be burnt to give energy for heating.

- In Brazil they grow sugar cane, and then use the sugar to make
  alcohol. The alcohol is then used in cars, instead of petrol.

- Rotting plants and animal manure can make a gas called methane.
  This is like the gas you use in a Bunsen burner.
  If the plants rot in a closed tank, called a **digester**, the gas can be
  piped away. This is often used in China and India:

▶   Design a digester to use straw and dung. Think about:
   - It needs an air-tight tank.
   - How will you get the gas out, to a cooker**?**
   - How will you get the straw and dung in**?**
f   Draw a sketch of your design and label it.

A cow-dung digester in India

Solar energy

The energy in the Sun's rays is called **solar energy**.

g Why is the Earth the only planet in the Solar System with life on it?

h Which parts of the Earth get the least energy?

▶ Look at these 3 ways of using solar energy, and answer the questions:

A **solar cell** transfers some of the sunlight into electricity.

In the photograph, some solar cells are being used to run an electric water-pump:

You may have a calculator that uses a solar cell.

i What are the advantages and disadvantages of a solar-powered calculator?

j Why are solar cells not widely used?

A **solar cooker** has a curved mirror, to focus the Sun's rays:

k Is the mirror convex or concave?

▶ Design your own solar cooker. Think about:
  • Should the mirror be large or small?
  • Should the mirror be fixed or adjustable?
  • Where should you put the pan or kettle?

l Draw a sketch of your design and label it.

Some houses have a **solar panel** on the roof.
The water in the panel is heated by the Sun, and stored in a tank:

▶ Design your own solar panel system. Think about:
  • Hot water rises, cold water falls.
  • Black cars get hotter in the Sun than white cars.
  • Objects get hotter behind glass (like in a greenhouse).

m Draw a sketch of your design and label it.

Things to do

1 Copy and complete:
a) Energy from the Sun is called . . . . energy.
b) Green plants contain a chemical called . . . . This absorbs the Sun's . . . . and uses it to make . . . . and . . . . This process is called . . . .
c) The materials that plants and animals are made from, are called . . . .

2 How does a greenhouse use solar energy to help gardeners?

3 For each of these food-energy chains, write them in the correct order:
a) chicken, Sun, human, corn
b) seaweed, Sun, seagull, snail
c) ladybird, rose, greenfly, Sun
d) grasshopper, lizard, Sun, grass, hawk
e) bee, human, flower, Sun, honey
f) dead leaves, frog, Sun, earthworm, tree

4 What are:
a) the advantages, and
b) the disadvantages of a solar panel?

From fossils to fuels

A fossil in coal

▶ What is a **fuel?**
Write down as many fuels as you can think of.

▶ Coal, oil and natural gas are important fuels. Read the sections below and then answer questions **a** to **j**.

How was coal formed?

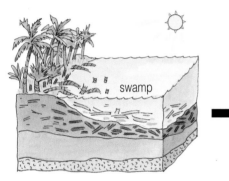

300 million years ago, plants store the Sun's energy. Dead plants fall into swampy water. The mud stops them from rotting away.

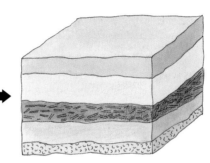

As the mud piles up, it squashes the plants.
After millions of years under pressure, the mud becomes rock and the plants become **coal**.

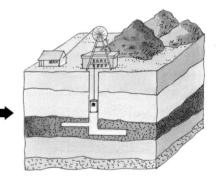

To reach the coal, miners dig shafts and tunnels. There is probably enough coal to last 300 years.
Fossils of plants are sometimes found in lumps of coal.

How was oil formed?

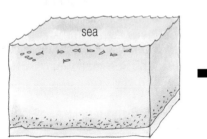

Tiny animals live in the sea.
When they die, they fall into the mud and sand at the bottom, and don't rot away.

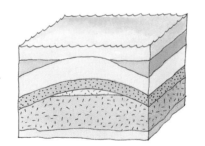

Over millions of years they get buried deeper by the mud and sand.
The pressure changes the mud and sand into rock, and the dead animals become **crude oil** and **natural gas**.

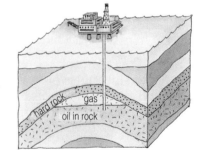

The oil can move upwards through some rocks, but if it meets a layer of hard rock it is trapped (with the gas).
An oil rig can drill down to release it.
There is enough oil to last about 40 years.

a What is a fossil**?**

b Why are coal, oil and gas called fossil fuels**?**

c Explain in your own words how coal was formed.

d Give 2 similarities and 2 differences between the way coal was formed and the way oil was formed.

e Diana says, "The energy stored in coal, oil and gas all comes from the Sun." Explain this statement.

f Oil, coal and gas are called **non-renewable** resources. What do you think this means**?**

g Why will fossil fuels eventually run out**?**

h How old will you be when the oil runs out**?**

i Why is coal usually found in layers**?**

j Why are some rocks called sedimentary rocks**?**

Renewable and non-renewable

Some sources of energy are **renewable**.
For example, wood. It can be burnt, but a new tree can be planted.
Solar energy is also a renewable resource.

However coal, oil and gas are **non-renewable** resources. Once we have used them up, they are gone forever.

Uranium is another non-renewable resource. It is used in nuclear power stations. Supplies of uranium will run out eventually.

Making electricity

The graphs show the sources of energy used to generate electricity in 3 countries:

k Which country generates the most electricity?

l List the energy sources used to make electricity in the UK.

m Hydroelectric sources are not used much in the UK. Why is this?

n Which is the main source in Norway? Why is this?

o What do you notice about the use of nuclear power in the 3 countries?

p Which of the sources is renewable?

q Coal has been used a lot in the UK, but coal-fired power stations can produce a lot of **acid rain**. What would be your solution to this problem, taking into account:
i) the environment?
ii) coal-miners and their families?

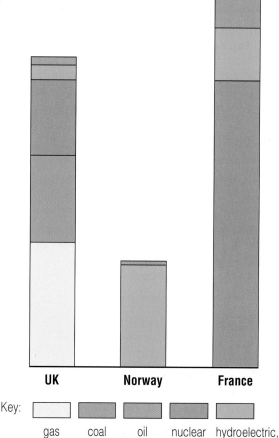

Key:

gas   coal   oil   nuclear   hydroelectric, biomass, wind

The nuclear debate

The world is running out of energy, but many people are against the use of nuclear energy.

In a group, use the Help Sheets to discuss your ideas *for* or *against* using nuclear energy.

Things to do

1 Copy and complete:
a) Coal, oil and . . . . are fossil . . . .
They have taken . . . . of years to form.
b) Coal, oil, gas and uranium are non- . . . . sources of energy.
c) Some renewable sources of energy are:

2 Explain in your own words how oil and natural gas were formed.

3 Why is it important to avoid wastage of fossil fuels?

4 Make a table to show how people could save non-renewable fuels. For example:

Action to be taken	How it saves fuel
don't overfill the kettle	uses less electricity

21d Burning fuels

▶ What fuels do you use in your home? Make a list.

▶ Look at this picture of a *match* burning:

Wood is a fuel. It has potential energy stored in it.
This energy can only be transferred if the fuel burns with
the oxygen in the air.
It is a chemical reaction.

Burning fuels are used in power stations and in car engines.

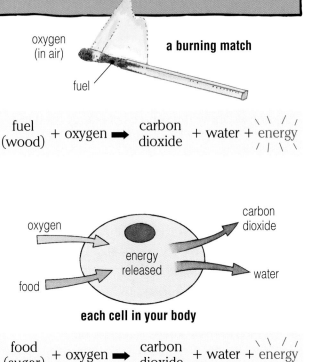

a burning match

$$\text{fuel (wood)} + \text{oxygen} \rightarrow \text{carbon dioxide} + \text{water} + \text{energy}$$

As you already know, the *cells* in your body 'burn' the
food that you eat – but of course there aren't any flames!
Your blood carries sugar (from your food) and oxygen
(from the air you breathe) to all the cells in your body:

The *same* chemical reaction releases the energy.

This is called **respiration**.
You use the energy to keep warm and to move around.

each cell in your body

$$\text{food (sugar)} + \text{oxygen} \rightarrow \text{carbon dioxide} + \text{water} + \text{energy}$$

Using fuels in a power station

Follow the diagram to see how fuel is burned, to generate electricity:

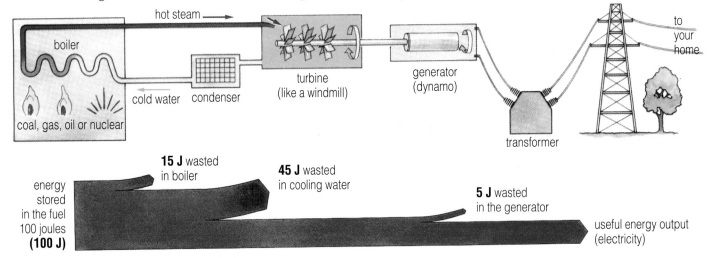

a   What does the boiler do?
b   What does the steam do to the turbine?
c   What does the generator do?
d   For every 100 joules of energy in the fuel, how much comes out as useful energy?
e   What is the **efficiency** of the power station?
f   Where is most energy wasted? Can you think of a way of using this wasted energy?

Comparing engines

A car engine burns fuel. The energy from the fuel makes the engine turn, so the car moves.

A human body is also a kind of engine:

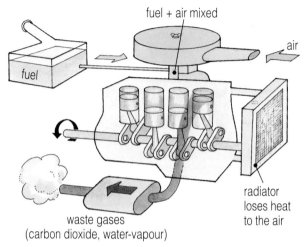

fuel + air mixed

air

fuel

radiator
loses heat
to the air

waste gases
(carbon dioxide, water-vapour)

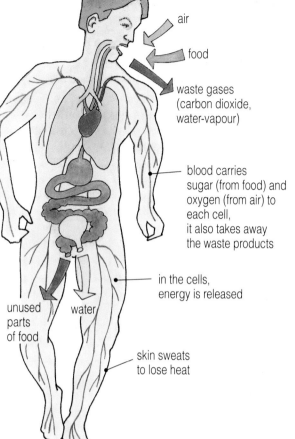

air

food

waste gases
(carbon dioxide,
water-vapour)

blood carries
sugar (from food) and
oxygen (from air) to
each cell,
it also takes away
the waste products

in the cells,
energy is released

unused
parts
of food

water

skin sweats
to lose heat

For each question **g** to **m**, write down the answer, first for the **car engine** and then for the **human engine**.

g What fuel does the engine use?

h What does it use the fuel for?

i Where is the fuel used ('burned') in the engine?

j How does the engine get its oxygen?

k How does the engine get rid of unwanted heat?

l What waste substances are produced in the engine?

m How does the engine get rid of these waste products?

Investigating sweeteners

Plan an investigation to compare the **amount of energy** in some **sugar** and in some **artificial sweetener**.

- How will you make them burn?
- What will you do with the energy from the burning fuel?
- How will you make it a fair test? And safe!

Ask your teacher to check your plan, and then do the investigation.

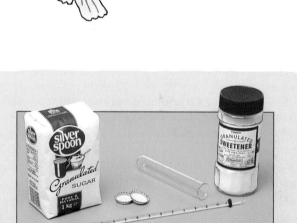

Things to do

1 Copy and complete:
a) In order to burn, a fuel needs . . . .
    It usually gets this from the . . . .
b) The chemical equation for a fuel burning is:
c) In the cells in my body, energy is released when sugar (from my . . . .) reacts with . . . . (from the . . . . I breathe).
d) This is called . . . .
e) The chemical equation for this is:

2 Do a flow-chart to show how the energy in a coal-mine makes a cup of tea for you.

3 Draw an Energy Diagram for:
a) a burning match,
b) a cell in your body.

4 Explain the correct way to deal with:
a) a chip-pan fire,   b) a petrol fire,
c) an electric blanket on fire.

Running out of energy

We need energy for running our homes, transport and factories. Most of this energy comes from burning **fuels**.
Fuels store energy.

▶ Make a list of all the fuels you can think of. The picture will help you.

▶ Write down 3 things about your life that would be different if we did not have these fuels.

Coal, oil and natural gas are called **fossil fuels**. They were made from plants and animals that lived on Earth many millions of years ago.

▶ Look at the table of data and interpret it to answer these questions:

a Which fuel is easiest to set alight?

b Which fuel burns most cleanly?

c Which fossil fuel is solid?

d Which is the liquid that gives us petrol?

e Which fuel gives most energy when 1 gram of it is burned?

f The price of these fuels varies from year to year, but from the table which is the cheapest?

Fossil fuel	Easy to light?	Burns cleanly?	Amount of energy released	Approx. amount of energy for £1
natural gas	very easy	yes	55 kJ per gram	230 000 kJ
oil	yes	no	45 kJ per gram	250 000 kJ
coal	no	no	30 kJ per gram	300 000 kJ

Fossil fuels are **non-renewable** sources of energy. Once we have used them up, they are gone for ever!

▶ On the time-chart find:
  • the year you were born
  • where we are now
  • the year when you will be 40 years old
  • the year in which you will be 60.

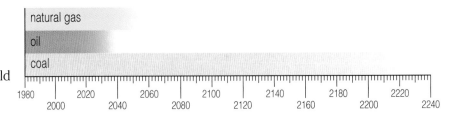

g From this chart, what do you notice about the fuels?

h What can you predict about your life when you are 60?

▶ There are other sources of energy called **renewable** sources. For example: energy from the wind (as in a windmill).

i How many other renewable sources of energy can you name? Make a list.

Energy consumption

Fossil fuels are used in some power stations to make electricity.

We can also get energy from:
- **nuclear power stations**. They use uranium but this is getting scarce.
- **hydro-electric power stations**. They use the potential energy from water stored in high dams.
- **biomass**. This is the energy stored in growing plants, such as wood.

▶ Look at the pie-charts and interpret them to answer these questions:

j List the energy sources used in the UK.

k What was the percentage for natural gas in the UK? Where do you use natural gas in school?

l Which were the biggest sources of energy for the UK in 2001?

m Which was the smallest source of energy for the UK? Why is this?

n Which source was not used in the UK?

o Which of the sources are **renewable**?

p In your group, compare the two charts and suggest some reasons why you think they are different.

q **Predict** what you think the world pie-chart will look like when you are 60.

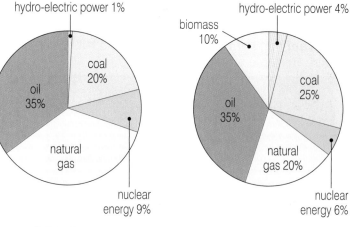

UK in 2001   World in 2001

World trade in energy

The graph shows the energy sold commercially each year:

r Which of the resources in not shown in 1970?

s Why is biomass not shown at all?

t What happened to world demand during these 30 years?

u Estimate the world energy demand in 2010.

v Discuss what the graph will look like when you are 60. Can you predict its shape?

w Draw a pie-chart for the year 2000.

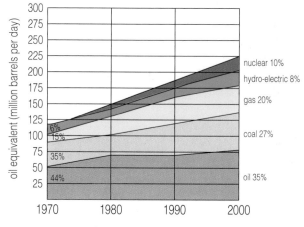

World energy sales

---

1 Petrol, coal and potatoes are fuels. Explain how you could use each of these fuels to keep you warm.

2 Make a survey of all the fuels used in your home.

3 Draw a poster advertisement to promote a fuel. Choose one of these: oil, gas, wood or coal.

4 Make a table showing how people could save fossil fuels. For example:

Action to be taken	How it saves fuel
Drive smaller cars	Uses less petrol

5 Make a list of the properties of an **ideal** fuel.

Things to do

Energy for ever?

▶ What is meant by a **non-renewable** resource?
Name 4 non-renewable sources of energy.

What is a **renewable** source of energy?
You have already studied 2 renewable sources,
biofuel and **solar energy** (on pages 58–59).
Here are some more:

Wind energy
Windmills have been used for centuries.
Modern wind-turbines are huge. One advantage is that the wind blows most when we need more energy – in winter.

Why does this energy come originally from the Sun?

Geothermal energy
This geyser is spurting out hot water. This is because deep inside the Earth it is very hot.
If a very deep hole is drilled, cold water can be piped down, to return as hot water or steam.

Wave energy
Waves are caused by the wind. They contain a lot of energy but it is hard to make use of it.
One idea is to have floats that move up and down with the waves and so turn a generator.

Why does this energy come originally from the Sun?

Hydro-electric energy
Water stored by a dam has potential energy.
When it runs down-hill, its kinetic energy can turn a turbine or a water-wheel. This can turn a generator to make electricity.

Why does the energy come originally from the Sun?
Why is this resource impossible in some countries?

Tidal energy
The tides are caused by the pull of the Moon and Sun.
In some places there are very high tides.
The water can be trapped behind a barrier, like a dam:
Then it can be used like hydro-electric energy.

Joule Island

Joule Island is a remote island, in the Pacific Ocean.
You are in a team of 30 scientists who will be staying on the island for 3 years to study it.
Your task is to provide all the energy that the team will need.

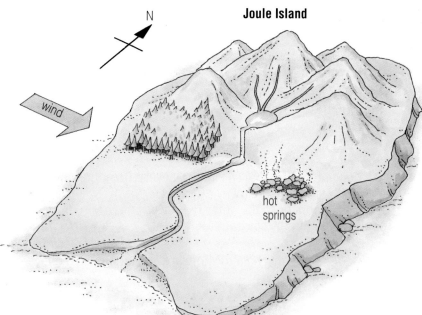

Joule Island

Study the island:

a There are no fossil fuels on the island, and it is 500 km to the mainland. What would be the advantages and disadvantages of setting up a power station which used coal or oil?

b What renewable energy resources are there on the island?

c Which natural resource on the island should be carefully conserved?

The island has sunny days but cold nights.
The wind blows most days, but not in summer.
The hot springs are at a temperature of 80°C.

d The team is going to build huts to live in.
Name 2 ways in which the huts could be heated.

e Design a way of supplying hot water for washing.

f Design a way of supplying energy for cooking food.

g The team has a refrigerator for medicines which have to be kept cool at all times, day and night.
Design a way of supplying electricity continuously for the refrigerator.

h Your teacher will give you a picture of the island. Mark on the picture:
 • where you would build the huts, and
 • where you would build any energy installations you have designed, and
 • show how the energy would be transferred to the huts.

i When summer comes, you find that the fresh-water sources tend to dry up. How does this affect your energy plan? Design a way to get over this.

j For some experiments on the island you need some gas for a Bunsen burner. Describe 2 ways to provide this.

---

1 Copy and complete:
a) Fossil fuels like coal, ... , and natural gas will eventually run out. They are non-. . . . resources.
b) Nuclear energy is also a . . . . resource.
c) Other energy resources are called . . . .
d) There are 7 renewable sources of energy. They are:

2 Which of the 7 renewable sources get their energy originally from the Sun?

3 Design the scientists' huts for Joule Island. You should design them so that:
 • they have sleeping, leisure and work areas, and
 • they will be cool during the day and warm at night.

Things to do

Questions

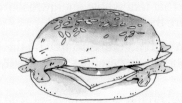

1 Draw Energy Diagrams for:
a) a torch
b) a bonfire burning
c) a boy kicking a football.

2 A car engine is only 25% efficient. Of every 100 joules in the petrol, only 25 J actually make the car move.
a) What happens to the other 75 joules?
b) Draw an Energy Diagram for the car.

3 Draw a food-energy chain to show how the energy in a cheeseburger comes from the Sun to:
a) the cheese
b) the bread.

4 In a solar cell, for every 100 joules of solar energy shining on it, only 10 J is transferred to useful energy in electricity.
a) What happens to the other 90 joules?
b) What is the efficiency of the solar cell?
c) Draw an Energy Diagram of this, with the width of the arrows to scale. Label it.

5 Think about what life would be like without coal, oil, or natural gas. (Remember that petrol and plastics come from oil.)
You can present your ideas in a list, or in a story, or on a poster.

6 When you switch on a light, it is the result of a long chain of events. These are listed below, in the wrong order. Write them down in the correct order.
A plants take in energy from the Sun
B coal is burnt in oxygen (in air)
C water is heated, to make steam
D the Sun produces energy
E plants change to coal over millions of years
F steam makes a turbine turn
G the generator produces electricity
H electricity heats up the lamp and it shines
I the turbine turns a generator
J electricity travels through wires to your home

7 A typical British family uses energy like this:

Heating the house	40%	Heating water	10%
Transport	25%	Food eaten	5%
Electrical goods	15%	Cooking	5%

a) Draw a pie-chart or a bar-chart to show this information.
b) Where should they look first in order to save money?

Chemical reactions

22

Have you seen fireworks that look as good as this?
Each flash of light means that a chemical reaction is happening.

Some reactions are much slower.
They seem less exciting.
But *all* chemical reactions are important
. . . they are keeping you alive today!

Making new materials is a very important job for a scientist.

▶ Look at the picture below. What materials have scientists helped to make? Write a list. For example, glass for windows.

Do you remember burning magnesium ribbon?
This was an example of making a new substance.

A change which makes a new substance is called a **chemical change**.
A **chemical reaction** must happen.
The new substance is called a **product**.

Burning magnesium

$$\text{magnesium} + \text{oxygen} \xrightarrow[\text{reaction}]{\text{chemical}} \text{magnesium oxide}$$

a What is the product of this reaction?

b How do you know a new substance has been made?

▶ Your teacher may show you 2 changes.
Which one do you think is a *physical change*?
Which one is a *chemical change*?
Use the table below to help you.

Physical changes	Chemical changes
no new substances made	new substances made
easy to reverse	not easy to reverse

Heating
copper carbonate

Melting
wax

▶ Which of **c** to **h** are chemical changes?
(Hint: Can you get the materials you started with back again easily? Is it *reversible*?
or Have new substances been made?)

c Baking a cake.	**f** Dissolving salt in water.
d Striking a match.	**g** Burning some toast.
e Making ice cubes.	**h** Baking clay.

Notice any change?

Here are some tests for you to do. In each one find out what happens when you mix the substances.

For each test, say if you think a new substance is made. Before you start, think about how to record your findings.

- You must wear safety glasses.
- Only use small amounts of the substances. ***Do not use more than the instructions tell you to***.

⚠️ eye protection toxic chemicals

1. 3 cm^3 dilute sulphuric acid $+ \frac{1}{2}$ spatula measure of copper carbonate
2. 3 cm^3 dilute sulphuric acid $+ 3 \text{ cm}^3$ sodium hydroxide solution
3. 3 cm^3 vinegar $+ \frac{1}{2}$ spatula measure of bicarbonate of soda
4. 3 cm^3 water $+ \frac{1}{2}$ spatula measure of copper oxide
5. 3 cm^3 lead nitrate solution $+ 3 \text{ cm}^3$ potassium iodide solution
6. 3 cm^3 dilute sulphuric acid $+$ copper foil
7. 3 cm^3 water $+$ iron nail
8. 3 cm^3 dilute sulphuric acid $+ 2 \text{ cm}$ of magnesium ribbon
9. 3 cm^3 copper sulphate solution $+ 1$ spatula measure of iron filings

Look at your results for all the tests.
How do you know if a new substance has been made?

i Make a list of things that can happen when a new substance is made.
These things can tell you that there has been a **chemical reaction**.

---

1 Copy and complete:
a) A change which makes new substances is called a c . . . . change.
b) This change is called a c . . . . r . . . .
c) The new substance is called a p . . . .
d) A p . . . . of the r . . . . between carbon and oxygen is called c . . . . d . . . .

2 Make a list of some chemical changes that happen around your home.
Draw a picture to show one of the changes happening.

3 Do a survey of a car.
Make a list of all the materials used to make the car.
Say whether these are natural or made materials.
Why is each material right for its job?

Material	Natural? or Made?	Why is it used?

4 The Earth's resources, such as sea, crude oil, air, rocks and plants are called ***raw materials***.

Think of a raw material which is made into a useful substance.
Draw a poster to show this change in an interesting way.
What are the uses of the substance made?

Things to do

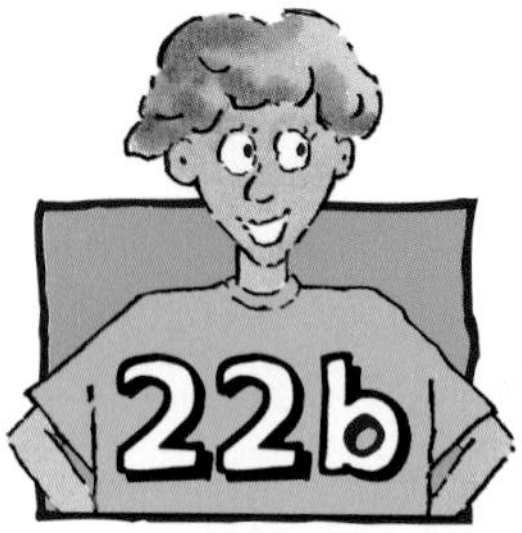
22b

Getting the iron

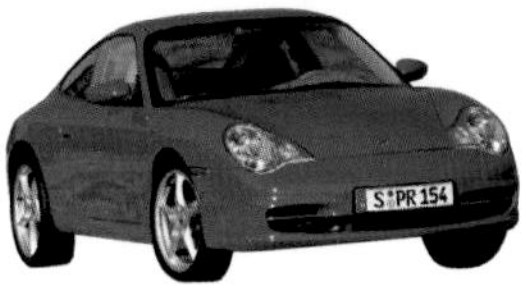
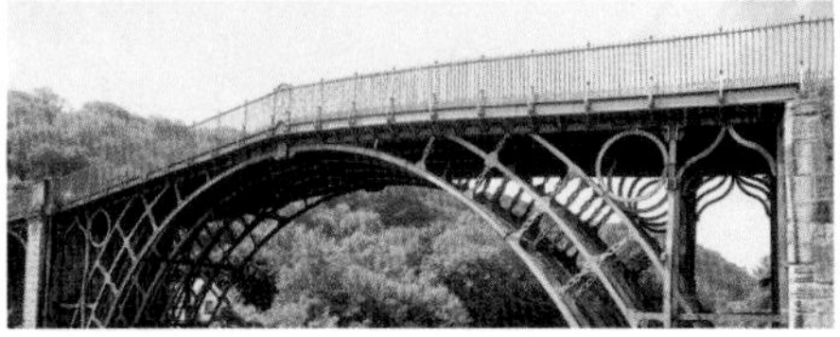
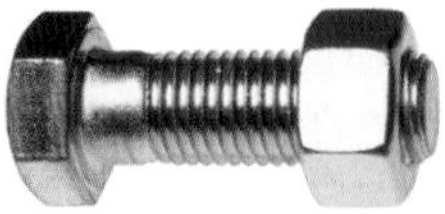

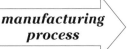

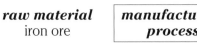

Look at the photos above. What do all the objects have in common? There's more than one answer to this! But if you've read the top of the page, you've probably said they all contain ***iron***. You're right!

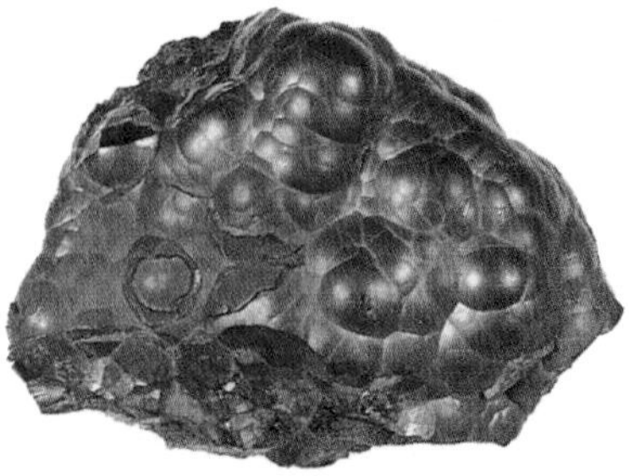
Iron ore

Look at the photo of the rock. It is iron **ore**.
It comes from the ground. The ore itself isn't useful. But it can be made into other useful materials.

raw material iron ore → ***manufacturing process*** → ***useful products*** iron and steel

▶ Why do you think iron is so useful?

a Make a list of the properties of iron.

b What is steel? Does it have any advantages over iron?

Every day the chemical industry makes many useful products from raw materials. This can involve lots of **chemical reactions**.
Let's look at the reactions needed to make iron.

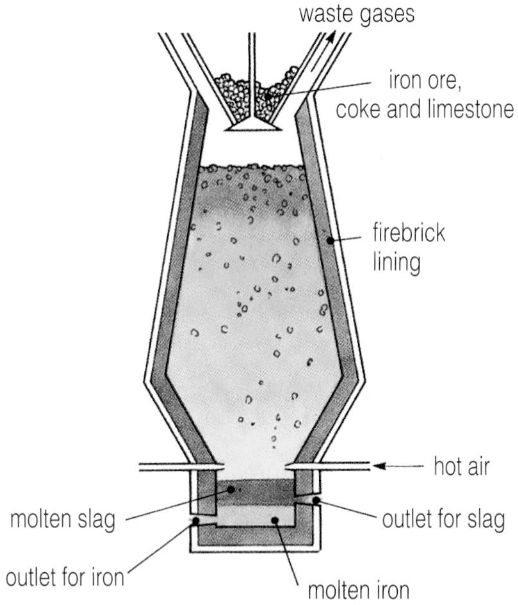
waste gases
iron ore,
coke and limestone
firebrick
lining
hot air
molten slag
outlet for slag
outlet for iron
molten iron

The blast furnace

The most common ore of iron is called haematite. It is iron oxide. This is a compound of iron and oxygen. To get the iron from this ore, we need to remove the oxygen. This is done in a **blast furnace**:

$$\text{iron oxide} \xrightarrow{\text{remove the oxygen}} \text{iron}$$

We say the iron oxide is **reduced**.
Reducing means ***taking the oxygen away***.

In the blast furnace there is some coke, a form of carbon.
This helps to take the oxygen away.
It does this at a temperature of 1200°C.
But there are lots of impurities in the iron ore.
Limestone is used to get rid of these.
In the heat, limestone breaks down. It changes to new substances.

$$\underset{\text{(limestone)}}{\text{calcium carbonate}} \xrightarrow{\text{heat}} \text{calcium oxide} + \text{carbon dioxide}$$

The calcium oxide then reacts with some impure substances in the iron ore. It makes a liquid slag.
It's very hot inside the blast furnace so the iron made is melted (molten).

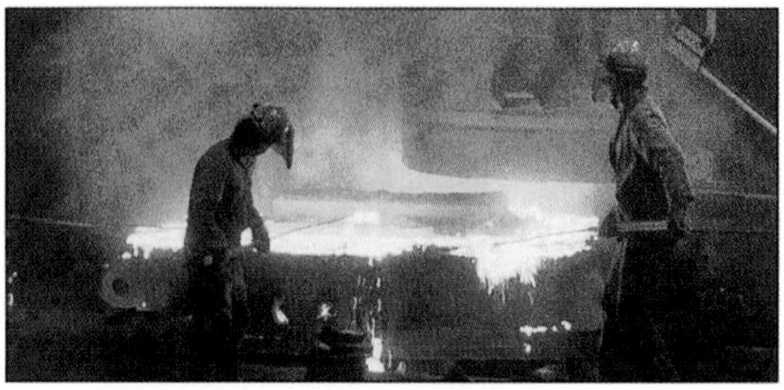

c Name 3 substances used in the blast furnace.

d Why is the blast furnace lined with fire brick**?**

e Name one gas which will be a 'waste gas'.

f Why do blast furnaces work every day and night, all year round**?**

g Why is iron the cheapest of all metals**?**

A blast furnace

Heating limestone

One of the reactions in the blast furnace involves heating limestone (calcium carbonate). You can see what happens for yourself.

Before you start to heat:

- Ask your teacher to check your apparatus.
- Make sure you know how to stop suck-back (remove the lime water before you stop heating the limestone).
- Think about why you use lime water in the experiment.

Heat the limestone gently at first, then more strongly.

h What happens**?**

i Write a word equation for this chemical change.

Use this experiment to help you plan an investigation on some other carbonates.

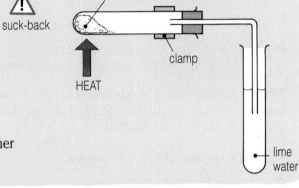

Investigating carbonates

Which carbonate changes the fastest when heated**?**
Your teacher must check your plan.
If there is time you may be able to carry out the investigation.

j Heat changes all 3 carbonates.
Write word equations for these chemical changes.

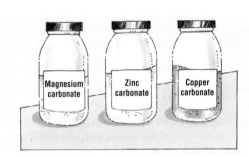

---

1 Copy and complete using the words in the box:

manufacturing	furnace	oxygen
raw	coke	impurities	hot
ore	carbonate	product

A . . . . process changes a . . . . material into a useful . . . . Iron . . . . is made into iron in the blast . . . .
The iron ore is reduced. This means its . . . . is removed. . . . . is a form of carbon which helps to reduce iron ore. Limestone is calcium . . . . It breaks down in the heat. It is used to get rid of . . . . The iron made is melted because it is so . . . . in the furnace.

2 The words in the box are ores.

| bauxite | galena |
| malachite | magnetite |

a) Use books to find out which metal comes from each ore.
b) Write down one use of each metal.
c) What things affect the price of any metal?
d) Iron is quite cheap. Name 2 metals that cost more.

3 Limestone is an example of a **sedimentary** rock.
a) Explain how this type of rock forms.
b) Name 2 other types of rock. Write a few lines to explain how each one forms.

Things to do

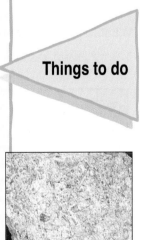

A burning problem

Have you ever seen this symbol?
This is called the **fire triangle**.

a Why are the words HEAT, OXYGEN and FUEL written on the fire triangle?

b Use the fire triangle to explain what you must do to stop a fire.

You have already learnt about some fuels in your science lessons.

▶ Make a list of all the fuels you can think of.
Choose 3 which you think are the most important. Explain why.

A fuel is a substance which burns in oxygen to give us energy.
New substances are made as the fuel burns. Burning is a **chemical reaction**. The reaction is between the fuel and the oxygen gas in the air. This chemical change is also called **combustion**.
When the fuel burns it makes **oxides**.

fuel + oxygen ──────▶ oxides + energy

This is an **exothermic** reaction.
This means heat (energy) is given out.

Burning a fuel

Bread is an example of a fuel. It is fuel for your body.
Usually you don't want to burn the toast. But in the next experiment you will do just that!

Hold the bread in tongs over a heat-resistant mat.
Observe the bread very carefully.
Heat the bread until it no longer burns.
Write down everything you see.   ⚠ eye protection

What happens to the bread during burning?

In your group, discuss your ideas about burning.

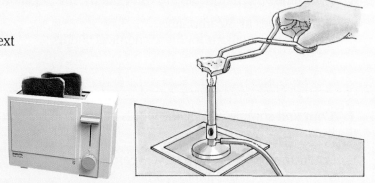

Bread is like most fuels. It contains hydrogen and carbon.

That must mean it makes oxides of carbon and hydrogen when it burns.

Where do the oxides go?

c When carbon reacts with oxygen it makes . . . .

d When hydrogen reacts with oxygen it makes . . . . This is usually called . . . .

e Where **do** the substances made in **c** and **d** go?

Burning candles . . . what do you think?

A candle is made of wax. Candle wax is a fuel. It contains the elements **carbon** and **hydrogen**.

eye protection

- Predict what will happen when a beaker is put over a burning candle.
  What do you expect to see**?**

- Now try the experiment. Were you right**?**

How do you test for carbon dioxide and water?

How do we know we are making these compounds?

A more difficult prediction . . .
- Predict what will happen when a beaker is put over candles of three different heights.
  Which candle do you think will go out first**?**
  Explain your ideas.

- Now try the experiment. Were you right**?**
  Try to explain what happened.

candle wax + oxygen ⟶ carbon dioxide + water + energy

This reaction is an example of an **oxidation**.
A substance has **gained** oxygen.

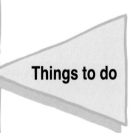

Things to do

1 Write 2 or 3 lines about each of the following words to explain what it means.
a) fuel c) oxide
b) combustion d) exothermic

2 You need to take great care when using fuels. Draw a poster to warn people of the dangers.

3 Ethanol is a substance which is made from carbon, hydrogen and oxygen. Copy and complete the word equation to show what you think happens when it burns.

ethanol + ... ⟶ .... + water + ...

4 Collect some newspaper cuttings about fires. For each fire try to find out:
a) How the fire started.
b) Whether the fire could have been prevented.
c) How the fire was put out.
Record all the information in a table.

5 Fuels can be solids, liquids or gases. Give one example of each type.
What are the advantages of
a) a **solid** fuel?
b) a **liquid** fuel?
c) a **gaseous** fuel?

22d Bubbling reactions

What can you remember about **respiration?**

Every time you breathe, a chemical reaction is taking place.

a What happens when Jane breathes out into the lime water?

b What happens when Tom breathes out onto the cold window?

You get energy out of your food in respiration.

c Complete the word equation for respiration:

sugar + oxygen ⟶ . . . . + ... + energy

Respiration is an **exothermic** reaction.

d What does exothermic mean?

e Think about respiration and burning.
What are the similarities between these reactions?
Make a list of your ideas.

f Why do you get short of breath and hot in a race?

Fermentation

When **we** respire we use oxygen. It reacts with our food to make carbon dioxide, water and energy.
But some living things can respire **without** oxygen.
An example is a microbe called **yeast**.
Yeast is used to make wine. It uses up the sugar in fruit to make alcohol.
This process is called **fermentation**.

Drink	Made from
wine	grapes
brandy	grapes
beer	barley
whisky	barley
vodka	potato
cider	apples
saki	rice

Bubbling alcohol

Try your own fermentation using sugar.
Mix some yeast with about 4 g of sugar.
Add about 10 cm³ of warm water (about 35°C) and put it in a flask.
Leave the apparatus set up like the diagram shows.
Look at the flask after 10 minutes. What do you notice?
Look at the flask again after 45 minutes.

⚠️ **Carefully** smell the contents. What do you notice?

⚠️ **Do not attempt to drink this substance. It is very impure.**

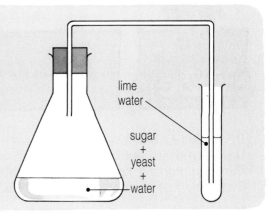

lime
water

sugar
+
yeast
+
water

The word equation for fermentation is

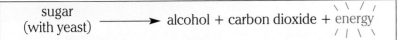

sugar
(with yeast) $\longrightarrow$ alcohol + carbon dioxide + energy

g In what ways is this reaction **like** your respiration?

h In what ways is this reaction **different** to your respiration?

i Why is it dangerous to drink and drive?

j Some people think it's wrong to drink **any** alcohol. Do you agree? Discuss this in your group.

▶ Don't drink and drive.
Design your own poster to get this message across.

---

1 Copy and complete:
a) When we breathe, the products are . . . . , ... and . . . .
b) The products of fermentation are . . . . , ... and . . . .
c) An exothermic reaction is one in which heat . . . .

2 Remind yourself of the 'Bubbling alcohol' experiment above.
How do you know a reaction has taken place?
List your ideas.

3 Yeast is also used in bread-making.
Find out how bread is made.
Why is yeast used?
Why could this be called a **bubbling reaction**?

4 Breath tests can be used to see if drivers have been drinking too much alcohol.

a) Make a list of arguments **for** random breath-testing (testing any driver at any time).
b) Make a list of arguments **against** random breath-testing.

Things to do

Rusting parts

Do you have a bike**?**
Does anyone in your family have a car**?**
If so, you probably know about the problem of rust!
Every year rust causes millions of pounds worth of damage.

▶ Make a list of 4 problems caused by rust.

Many companies spend lots of money trying to stop rusting.
To know how to stop rusting, we must know what causes it.

Kris and Becky investigated the conditions needed for an iron nail to rust.
They set up 3 test-tubes and left them for a few days.

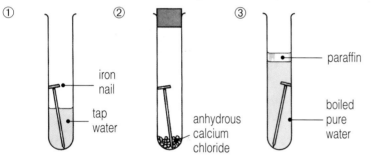

① iron nail / tap water

② anhydrous calcium chloride

③ paraffin / boiled pure water

▶ Copy the table. This shows the conditions inside the tubes.

Condition	Tube ①	Tube ②	Tube ③
air	✔	✔	✘
water	✔	✘	✔

Look at the conditions in tube ②.

a What do you think anhydrous calcium chloride does**?**

Look at the conditions in tube ③.

b What do you think happens when the water boils**?**

c Why is paraffin put on top of the boiled water**?**

After a few days, Kris and Becky checked the tubes.

d What 2 substances must be present for iron to rust**?**

Have you noticed any rusting at the seaside**?**

e Rusting happens faster by the sea. Why do you think this is**?**

. . . after a few days

Rusting is an **oxidation** reaction. The iron is **oxidised**.
This means it reacts with oxygen in the air.

f Complete the word equation:

iron + oxygen (with water) ⟶ . . . .

g What is the chemical name for rust**?**

Investigating rusting

The teacher found the group's results very interesting.
She wanted Kris and Becky to do a more detailed investigation.
She didn't give them any firm ideas, but set them a question:

Imagine you are Kris. Plan an investigation into the rusting of iron.
(If you need help with this, ask your teacher for a clue!)

Stopping the rot!

To stop iron from rusting we must protect it from air and water.
Here are some ways of doing this:

- **Painting**
  This is used to protect cars and large structures such as bridges.

- **Greasing or oiling**
  This is used on moving parts of machines.

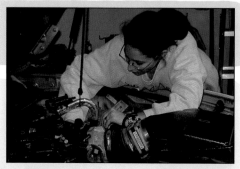

- **Plating**
  This is a thin coating of another metal which doesn't rust.
  Chromium plating is common. It gives an attractive, shiny effect.
  Zinc plating is also used. If the metal coating on the iron is zinc,
  the iron is said to be **galvanised**. Zinc will protect the iron even
  if it gets scratched.

Which rust prevention method would you use to:

h   protect a lawnmower in the winter**?**

i   protect a car bumper**?**

j   protect a school's iron gates**?**

Explain your choice in each case.

---

1   Copy and complete:
a)   . . . . and . . . . are needed for iron to rust.
b)   . . . . speeds up the rusting of iron.
c)   The chemical name for rust is . . . .
d)   Two methods to prevent rusting are . . . .
     and . . . .

2   Carry out a survey of cars near
where you live. **Look** at the cars,
don't touch. Take care.
Do certain makes of cars rust faster than
others?
Do some parts of the car rust faster than
other parts?
Present all your survey results in a table.
Write a summary report of your findings.

3   Different parts of a bike are prevented
from rusting in different ways.
Make a table to show the different bike parts
and the rusting prevention methods.

Parts of a bike	How is rusting prevented?
handlebars	

4   Do you think rusting happens to the
same extent in all parts of the world?
Explain your ideas about this.

Things to do

22f Fast or slow?

Do you think that rusting is a **fast** or **slow** reaction**?**

Chemical reactions happen at different rates.
Some are slow. Others are very fast.

▶ Think about the reactions below.
Say whether you think they are fast or slow reactions.

a Dynamite exploding.
b Wine fermenting.
c Milk turning sour.
d A sofa burning.
e Rocks being weathered.
f Magnesium burning in air.
g Developing a photograph.
h Wood burning.
i Baking a cake.

Wouldn't it be useful if we could change the rate of some reactions**?**

▶ Make a list of reactions which people would like to slow down.

Make a list of reactions which people would like to speed up.

Compare your answers with those of others in your group.

Do you all agree**?**

Chemical magic

Scientists can make reactions happen at different rates.
You may be impressed by your teacher's magic!
Your teacher will show you a reaction which makes a substance
called **iodine**.
It is easy to see when you've made iodine. (You might remember
the starch test from *Spotlight Science for Scotland 1*.)
When iodine is added to starch solution, it turns deep blue.
Your teacher will be able to make this blue colour appear at
different times . . . But you'll need to watch carefully.

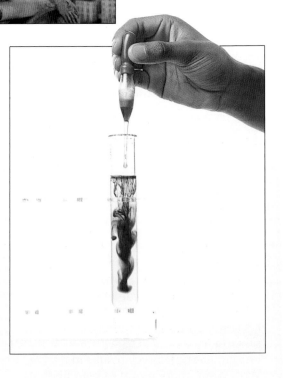

j Why do you think this reaction is called the **iodine clock?**
k How does your teacher do this? Is it **really** magic?

Speed it up!

You can investigate the reaction between magnesium and dilute hydrochloric acid.
How could this reaction be made faster or slower?
What is your hypothesis?
Do you have more than one idea to test?

Your teacher will give you some magnesium and some bottles of acid for the tests.

eye protection

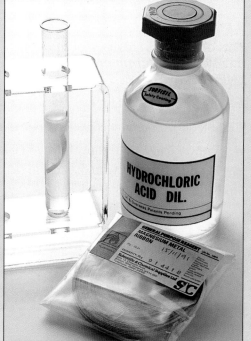

- Write down the tests you would like to do.
- You must write down the equipment you need.
- You must say *exactly* how much of each of the substances you need. Do this for each test.
- Show how you will record your results.

Let your teacher see your plans. If they are safe, you will be given the magnesium and acid. You can then start the investigation.

- Write down all the results from your tests.

- Look carefully at your results.
  Write a conclusion for your investigation.
  Your conclusion should start like this:

  The reaction rate can be changed by changing ....
  ....
  ....

  These are the **variables** which change the reaction rate.

- Are your results reliable?

- How could you improve your investigation?

Things to do

1 Write down 3 things which change the rate of a chemical reaction.

2 Sally was investigating the reaction between magnesium and hydrochloric acid. She had 5 sets of results.

Experiment	1	2	3	4	5
Time to collect 10 cm³ gas (in seconds)	15	6	43	15	29

a) Which experiment had the slowest rate?
b) Which experiment had the fastest rate?
c) In which 2 experiments were all the variables the same?
d) Sally says that the only thing she changed in the experiments was the temperature.
   Which experiment do you think took place at the highest temperature?

3 Magnesium reacts quickly with dilute hydrochloric acid.
Look at this list of other metals:

iron   copper   zinc   calcium

a) Which of these metals would react fastest with dilute hydrochloric acid?
b) Which metal will not react with dilute hydrochloric acid?
c) Imagine you have just discovered a new metal called Spotlight.
   Use the metal + acid reaction to plan an investigation to place Spotlight in the correct position in the Reactivity Series.

4 For magnesium and acid to react their particles must collide.
Try to explain your 'Speed it up!' results using the idea of moving particles.

22g   *A race against time!*

▶ Look at these photographs. They show a gargoyle at Lincoln Cathedral. They were taken 100 years apart.

a Which photo was taken most recently?

b What has caused the gargoyle to change over the years?

Lots of buildings are made of limestone. The chemical name for limestone is **calcium carbonate**. It reacts with acid to make carbon dioxide.

c How can you test for carbon dioxide gas?

Carbon dioxide can be collected **over water**.

d Draw a diagram to show how you can collect a gas over water.

e Limestone reacts with the acid in rain. Why do you think it is still used to make buildings?

Watching an acid attack!

Your teacher will show you limestone and acid reacting.
But before the experiment starts, make a prediction.
Do you think the mass of the flask and its contents will change during the reaction?
Will the mass . . . stay the same?
            . . . go up?
            . . . go down?
Predict what you think will happen. Why?

We can use an electronic balance to measure mass.
The electronic balance can be linked to a computer.
The computer will record the mass.

On paper sketch the shape of the graph you expect to see.
(Do not mark this book.)

Your teacher will now add the limestone to the acid.

f What happens to the mass of the flask and its contents?

g Why do you think this happens?

h Is this a fast or slow reaction?

i Why do you think the reaction at Lincoln Cathedral is slower?

j Why do we use a loose cotton wool plug in the experiment?

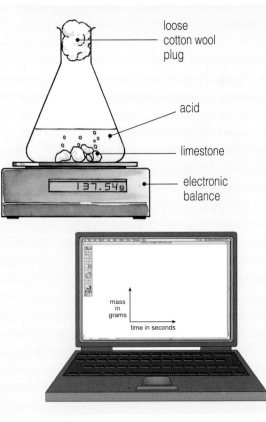

Time it to perfection

Do you remember the *iodine clock?* Your teacher *controlled* a chemical reaction.
You can control reactions too!

Your teacher will give you a time deadline for this task. You will need to work quickly. Everyone must be involved.
Will your group get the best result by the test deadline?

Your task is to:

Make a 100 cm³ sample of carbon dioxide gas in 60 seconds.

Your timing should be exact. You need to make *exactly* 100 cm³ of gas. (Not 99 cm³ or 101 cm³.)
Try to get as close to this volume as possible in the 60 seconds.
Use limestone and acid to make your carbon dioxide.

acid – eye protection

Your teacher will ask you to demonstrate your reaction to the other groups at the test deadline.

1   You have been asked to make a jelly for your brother's birthday party. The party is due to start in 2 hours! What will you do to dissolve the jelly cubes in water as quickly as possible?

2   Jan wants to make and collect a sample of carbon dioxide gas.
a)   Draw a labelled diagram of the apparatus she could use.
b)   Why can you collect carbon dioxide **over water**? What does this tell you about the gas?
c)   Describe 2 uses of carbon dioxide.

3   When magnesium ribbon reacts with an acid, it makes hydrogen gas. Ben measured the volume of gas given off every minute.

Time (minutes)	Volume (cm³)
0	0
1	20
2	35
3	45
4	50
5	52
6	52
7	52
8	52

a)   Draw a graph of these results.

b)   After how many minutes had the reaction finished?
c)   What volume of hydrogen had been collected at the end of the reaction?
d)   When was the reaction fastest . . . near the start or near the end?
e)   Give one way of making this reaction happen faster. Try to explain this by writing about **particles**. What happens to the particles of magnesium and acid in the reaction?

Things to do

Catalysts can help

▶ Think about how to make a reaction happen faster.
Make a list of the different ways to do this.

There is another way to change the rate of a reaction.
Catalysts can help.

You've already used **catalysts** in science before.
Do you remember making *oxygen*?

Manganese(IV) oxide is a catalyst. It makes the hydrogen peroxide
decompose (break down) quickly.

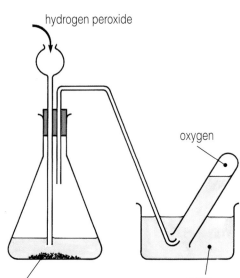

> A **catalyst** is a substance which changes the rate of a chemical
> reaction. A **catalyst** is not used up during the reaction.

Using catalysts

Have you ever looked *closely* at a packet of washing powder?
The powder in the photograph is like lots of others you can buy.
The list of ingredients on the box is interesting.
The powder contains **enzymes**.
On the box it says:

Ingredients	Function
Enzymes	Break down stains containing proteins e.g. blood, milk and stains containing fats e.g. body soils, cooking fat, etc.

So what are enzymes?
Enzymes are biological catalysts.
Enzymes in the washing powder help to break down stains quickly.
We say that the fat and protein in stains are **digested** by enzymes.

Enzymes help to make these.

Yeast contains enzymes.

▶ Look back in this topic.
Write a few lines to describe the reaction which used yeast.
(Hint: without the yeast, you'd still be waiting for the bubbles!)

Which is the better catalyst?

Hydrogen peroxide can decompose (break down).
It makes water and oxygen.

hydrogen peroxide ⟶ water + oxygen

You already know that manganese(IV) oxide is a catalyst for this reaction. It makes hydrogen peroxide decompose quickly.
But Leon has another idea:

> I want to make oxygen quickly. I think liver could be a better catalyst than manganese(IV) oxide.

HYDROGEN PEROXIDE

LIVER (RAW)

MANGANESE (IV) OXIDE

Plan an investigation to test Leon's idea.

Show your plan to your teacher. Then do the investigation.

Hydrogen peroxide can cause burns.
Wear eye protection.

---

1 Copy and complete:
A catalyst is a substance which . . . . the rate of a reaction.
A catalyst is not . . . . during the reaction.
Liver is a catalyst to make . . . . gas.
An . . . . is a biological catalyst.

2 Think about the reaction to make oxygen. Liver is a catalyst.
Does the temperature of the liver affect the rate of the reaction?
Plan an investigation to test this.

3 Catalysts can let reactions happen at a lower temperature than usual. Why do people in industry think catalysts are a good idea?

4 Find out about catalytic converters.
(Your local car showroom may let you have some leaflets.)
a) How do catalytic converters work?
b) What are the advantages of using them?
c) Are there any disadvantages?

Even though the use of unleaded fuel has cut exhaust emissions, new environment laws have been enforced. Every petrol-powered engine comes with a highly efficient 3-way catalytic converter as standard. This greatly reduces harmful emissions.

Things to do

Questions

1 Lee and Asha were looking at ways to prevent rust. Their teacher asked them which is the best method.

Who is right?
Plan an investigation to find out.

2 The UK chemical industry is the 5th largest in the world.
It makes many different products.
Draw a bar-chart or a pie-chart of these data:

Products made	Percentage of the industry (%)
Fertilisers	8
Organic materials	12
Inorganic materials	7
Soaps and toiletries	9
Pharmaceuticals	24
Plastics and rubbers	5
Paints and varnishes	8
Dyes and pigments	4
Specialised chemical products	23

3 A new iron and steel works is to be built in the UK.
Imagine you are in charge. You have to decide **where** to build it. What things would you need to think about?
Write a list.

4

> Coal is a better fuel than wood.

a) Do you think this statement is correct?
b) What makes a good fuel?
   What tests could you do to see which fuel is better?

5 a) Make a list of the main gases in the air.
b) Design an experiment to find out how much oxygen is in the air. (The diagram opposite might give you a clue about one possible way.)

candle on cork

water

6 Draw a poster to summarise everything you have learnt about reactions in this topic.
Use colour and pictures to make your poster interesting.

7 Read the memo and imagine you are Andrew.
Write at least half a page to advise Liz.

8 If you use more catalyst, does the reaction go faster?
Plan an investigation to find out.

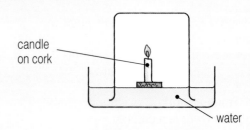

Spotlight Chemical Company URGENT
Memo to: Andrew   From: Liz
Making Spotlight X is too slow. We need to get the reaction to happen faster. Time costs money!
I understand you're using 20g of F13 and 10 cm³ of a solution of G44 to make Spotlight X.
Advise me how we could try to speed things up. Do you think we'll have any problems with your ideas?

Transferring energy

23

We need energy to keep us warm.

Heat energy can transfer from one place to another by conduction, convection and radiation.

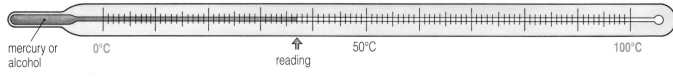
Warming up with energy

23a

mercury or alcohol   0°C   ↑ reading   50°C   100°C

a   What do you measure with a **thermometer?**

b   What is the reading on this thermometer**?**
(This is the temperature of a human body.)

c   What happens to water at i) 0°C**?**   ii) 100°C**?**

d   Explain how you think a thermometer works.

Heat (energy) and temperature

Thermal energy (heat) is ***not*** the same thing as temperature.
To understand this, let's compare these 2 things:

A white-hot spark

The tiny sparks are at a very high temperature, but
contain little energy because they are very small.

Each atom in the spark is **vibrating**.
Because it is very hot they are vibrating a lot.
But there are not many of them, so the total amount
of energy is small.

This idea about atoms is called the **Kinetic Theory**.

A bath-full of warm water

The water is at a lower temperature, but
it contains more energy.
This is because it contains more **atoms**.

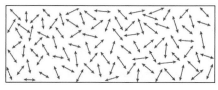

Each atom is vibrating at a low temperature,
but there are many of them.
There is a lot of thermal energy (heat).

Warming up water

Plan an investigation to see what happens when you give
the same amount of energy to different amounts of water.

- How will you make sure that you give the ***same***
amount of energy each time**?**

- Show your plan to your teacher, and then do it.

- Explain what happens, using these words:
energy   atoms   vibrating   temperature

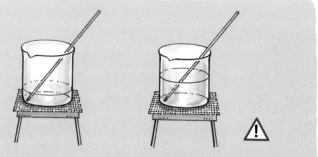

50 cm³   100 cm³

Energy on the move

Energy always travels *from* hot things *to* cold things.
There are 3 ways that the energy can be transferred:

Conduction	**Convection**	**Radiation**

  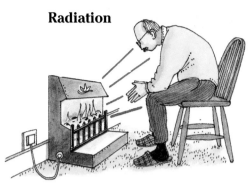

The metal handle gets too hot to hold. The energy has been **conducted** through the metal.

The metal is a good **conductor**. The wooden spoon is an **insulator**.

The air over the heater is warm. The hot air is rising upwards, in **convection** currents.

You get similar convection currents when you heat a beaker of water.

Radiant energy is travelling through the air, just like solar energy from the Sun.

The rays can travel through space, at the speed of light. They are also called **infra-red** rays.

▶ Here is a picture of a Bunsen burner heating up some gauze:

e After a while, the base feels warm at the point A. Why is this**?**

f If you put your hand at point B, it is hot. Why is this**?**

g If you put your hand near the red-hot gauze, at point C, it feels warm. Why is this**?**

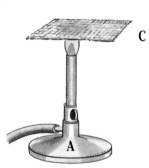
B

C

A

▶ Here is a 'model' to help us see the difference between these 3 ways. Three ways of getting a book to the back of the class:

1 Conduction: you can pass a book from person to person – just as the energy is passed from atom to atom.

2 Convection: you can carry the book to the back of the class – just as hot air moves in convection, taking the energy with it.

3 Radiation: a book can be thrown to the back of the class – rather like the way energy is radiated from a hot object.

---

1 Copy and complete:
a) When an object is heated, the energy makes the . . . . vibrate more. The hotter the object, the more the . . . . vibrate.
b) Energy travels from hot objects to . . . . objects by . . . . , or . . . . , or . . . .

2 Explain why a white-hot spark falling into a bath of water does not make the water hot.

3 Explain how an electric fire heats up a room.

Things to do

Conduction

▶ What would you feel if you stirred some hot soup with a metal spoon and with a wooden spoon? Can you explain this?

Energy on the move

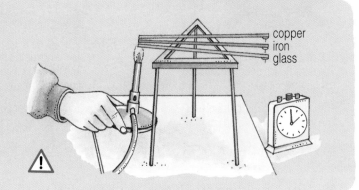

copper
iron
glass

- Set up 3 rods as shown, of copper, iron and glass:

- Use vaseline to fix a drawing-pin at the end of each rod.

- Then heat the ends of the rods equally, with a Bunsen burner.

- What happens? How long does it take for the first and second pins to fall off?

a Which way was energy flowing in the rods?

b Does the energy flow at the same rate through all the rods? Explain your answer.

c Which of these 3 materials would be best for making a pan? Explain your answer.

▶ The diagram shows how we can explain conduction, using the idea of atoms:

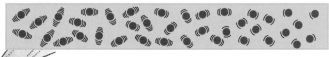

Energy is transferred from atom to atom along the bar. At the hot end, the atoms are vibrating a lot. As they bump into each other, the energy is passed along the bar.

▶ As you saw, copper is a good **conductor**.
In fact, **all metals are good conductors**.
Glass is an **insulator**.
Air is a very good insulator. We use this to keep us warm:

Birds fluff up their feathers in winter, to trap more air. The air is a good insulator and keeps them warm.

An anorak has a lot of trapped air. This slows down the transfer of thermal energy from your body.

Insulation in the loft of your house keeps you warm, and saves money. The material contains a lot of air.

Keeping warm

Your teacher will give you some materials that could be used for clothes, or to insulate your house.

Your job is to find out which of these materials is the best insulator.

- You could use a thermometer, or you could use a temperature sensor connected to a computer.
  What other equipment will you use?

- How will you make it a fair test?

- How will you record your results?

- Show your plan to your teacher, and then do it.

- Which material is best? **Why** do you think it is best?

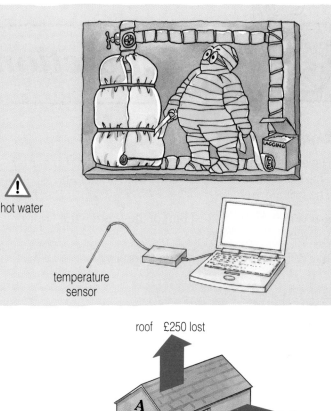

hot water

temperature sensor

Saving energy at home

Here are 2 houses:

One of them has been carefully insulated.

d Which house has **not** been insulated?

e What is the total heating bill for this house?

f Imagine you lived in this house.
Which parts would you insulate first?

g What is the total heating bill for the insulated house?

h All these places have been insulated:
walls, roof, floor, doors, windows.
  - Put them in order of the money saved.
  - Next to each one, write the amount of money saved.

i Draw an Energy Transfer Diagram for each house.

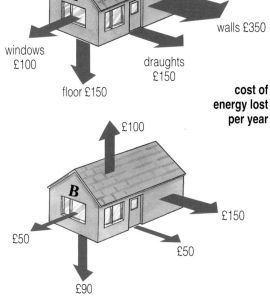

roof £250 lost

walls £350

windows £100

draughts £150

floor £150

cost of energy lost per year

£100

£150

£50

£50

£90

---

1 Copy and complete:
a) All metals are good . . . .
Copper is a very good . . . .
b) Glass is an . . . .
Air is a very good . . . .
c) Thermal energy passes through the bottom of a pan by . . . .
The energy is passed from each vibrating atom to the next . . . .

2 Make lists of where a) conductors and b) insulators are used in your home.

3 Write a letter to a pupil in your last school explaining what conduction is.

4 A double-glazed window has 2 sheets of glass, with air between.
Plan an investigation to see if double-glazing helps to insulate.
(Hint: you could use a beaker inside a bigger beaker.)

5 Explain this statement: "All the energy used in heating our homes is wasted."

Things to do

23c Convection and radiation

Convection

Have you ever noticed that flames always go upwards? This is because hot air is lighter than colder air. The hot air rises.

hot air rises

a Where is the hottest part of the room – the floor or the ceiling? Why?

b Why does smoke go up a chimney?

- Fill a beaker with cold water.
- Very gently, place a crystal of purple dye at the bottom and near the side:
- Put a **small** flame under the crystal.
- What happens? Explain what you see.

The water moves in a **convection current**. This carries the energy round the beaker.

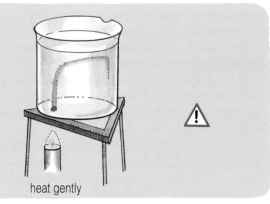
heat gently

▶ You get the same thing in a room.
The room is heated by the convection currents moving round:

c Why does a hot fire sometimes give you a cold draught on your feet?

On a sunny day, hot air currents can rise from the ground. Glider pilots can use them to lift their wings.

The Sun can cause very large convection currents, which we feel as **winds**.

▶ Use what you know about convection currents to explain what is happening in these photos:

convection current

Radiation

This sun-bather is getting hot:
Her body is **absorbing** energy.

d Where is the energy coming from?

e Could the energy have reached her by
conduction or convection? Explain
your answer.

This energy is called **solar energy** or **radiant energy**.
The rays include **infra-red rays** and **ultra-violet rays**.

f How can you use solar energy to cook food?

▶ Our bodies also **emit** (give out) radiation.
We **radiate** energy.
This is shown on the thermogram:

g Which part of the man is giving out
i) the most energy?
ii) the least energy?

h Use the key to estimate the temperature of his cheek.

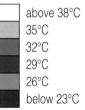

	above 38°C
	35°C
	32°C
	29°C
	26°C
	below 23°C

Melanie and Chris are discussing the colour of cars.

Melanie says, "I think black cars get hotter in the Sun."
Chris says, "Silver is brighter – I think a silver car will
get hotter."

Plan an investigation to see who is right.

• How will you make it a fair test?

• How many readings will you take?

• How will you show your results?

Show your plan to your teacher before you do the investigation.

1 Copy and complete:
a) Thermal energy (heat) can be carried
through a liquid by a . . . . current. The
hot liquid . . . . and the . . . . liquid falls.
b) . . . . currents also flow in air.
c) . . . . rays travel from the Sun through
empty space. This energy is called
. . . . energy or . . . . energy.
d) A black object absorbs more . . . . than
a silver one.
e) A silver surface . . . . the rays like a
mirror. This is used in a . . . . cooker.

2 Explain why:
a) Food cooks faster at the top of an oven.
b) Fire-fighters enter smoke-filled rooms by
crawling.
c) Houses in hot countries are often white.
d) There is shiny metal behind the bar of an
electric fire.

3 A potato is being cooked in boiling water.
Explain, as fully as you can, how energy gets
from the gas flame or hot-plate into the
middle of the potato.

Things to do

Physics at Work

A down-hill skier

Look at this photo of a down-hill skier:

a   What kind of energy does he have at the top of the hill**?**

b   What kind of energy is it changed into, as he moves down-hill**?**

c   There is some friction between his skis and the snow. What can you say about the temperature of the skis as he slides down**?**

d   What other friction force does he feel? Why is he crouching**?**

e   What has happened to all the energy when the race is finished**?**

An **elephant** sometimes gets too hot.

f   It has big ears. Explain how this helps it to cool down.

g   Explain carefully why it sometimes uses its trunk to spray water over its back.
How many reasons can you think of**?**

This **marathon runner** has just finished a race.

h   Why is she wearing a shiny plastic cover**?**

The **brakes** on this racing car are glowing red-hot.

i   Why is this**?**

j   What happens to this heat energy**?**

The diagram shows a **rocket-balloon**:

k   When the balloon is blown up, what kind of energy does it have**?**

l   Where did this energy come from**?**

m   When the air is released,
  • what happens to the balloon**?**
  • what happens to the energy**?**

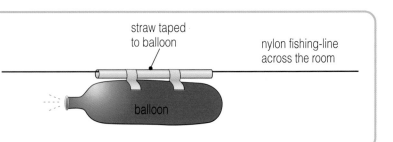

straw taped to balloon

nylon fishing-line across the room

balloon

An ordinary filament **light bulb** is only about 5% efficient. So for every 100 joules of electrical energy, only 5 joules are transformed to light energy.

n   What happens to the other 95 J?

An energy-saving bulb is also shown:
For every 100 J of electrical energy you get 25 J of light energy.

o   What is its efficiency?

p   Draw an Energy Transfer Diagram for each kind of bulb, to scale.

The diagram shows a side view of a **solar panel**. It is using solar energy to heat water for a house.

q   Which way is water flowing in the pipe?

r   Why is the hot water outlet at the ***top*** of the tank?

s   Explain how energy is transferred through the wall of the pipe to the water inside the tank. Use the idea of particles (atoms or molecules) in your explanation.

t   Why is there a black surface in front of the pipe and a shiny surface behind it?

u   Explain, step by step, how energy is transferred from the Sun to the hot water tap.

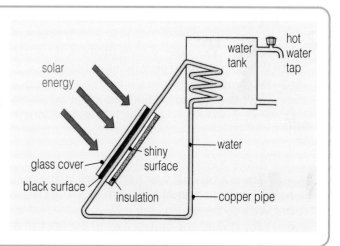

---

v   Why are chicks covered with fluffy feathers?

w   What happens if they get covered in oil?

Petrol consumption
The table shows some data for a car travelling on a level motorway.

x   Explain what the table is about.

y   Plot a graph of the data.

z   Explain what the graph tells you. Can you explain the shape?

speed (mph)	20	30	40	50	60	70
(km/h)	32	48	64	80	97	113
petrol used (cm³/km)	60	65	73	86	110	156

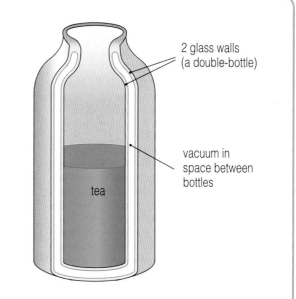

The cut-away diagram shows the *inside* of a 'thermos' **vacuum flask**, for keeping tea warm.

A   How does this design stop heat transfer by conduction?

B   How does this design stop heat transfer by convection?

Questions

1
a) Draw a diagram of a thermometer with a range from 0–100 °C.
b) On your thermometer label:
   i)   the freezing point of water with the letter F,
   ii) the boiling point of water with the letter B,
   iii) normal body temperature with the letter N.

2
a) Name the 3 different ways in which heat can be transferred.
b) Give one example of each method of transferring heat.
c) What happens to air when it is heated?
d) What happens to the atoms in a metal rod when it is heated?
e) How does loft insulation reduce heat loss from your home?
f) State 2 other ways in which heat loss from a home can be reduced.

3
a) Why is a fur coat warmer if worn inside-out?
b) Why does a carpet feel warmer to bare feet than lino or concrete?
c) Why do flames go upward?
d) Why should you crawl close to the floor in a smoke-filled room?
e) Why should fire-fighting suits be made of shiny material?

4
Jo has 2 mugs. They are the same except that one is black and one is white. They were filled with hot coffee and allowed to cool. Jo took their temperatures every 2 minutes, as shown in the table:

a) Plot a graph (of temperature against time) for each mug, on the same axes. Draw the lines of 'best fit'.
b) Which result do you think is wrong?
c) What is the temperature of the black mug after 3 minutes?
d) What is the difference in temperature after 9 minutes?
e) What conclusion can you draw from the graphs?

Time (min)	Black mug (°C)	White mug (°C)
0	90	90
2	68	78
4	55	67
6	45	58
8	37	52
10	31	43
12	26	37

5
Theo has 2 insulated pans of water at 20°C.
He gets 2 identical blocks of iron, both at 100°C, and puts one in pan A and one in pan B.
He measures the 'final' temperature that the water rises to, and puts his results in the table:

a) Explain carefully why the rise in temperature is less for pan B.
b) What is the final temperature of (i) the iron block in pan A? (ii) the iron block in pan B?
c) The 2 iron blocks were identical. Which one transferred more heat energy to the water? Explain your reasoning.
d) Explain the difference in the iron atoms when they were hot and when they were cold.

	Temperature of the water at the start (°C)	Temperature of the block at the start (°C)	Volume of water (cm³)	'Final' temperature of the water (°C)
A	20	100	500	35
B	20	100	1000	28

Electricity

24

What has your brain got in common with lightning, fire-alarms, and computers?
They all use electricity.

In the world today, there are electronic systems everywhere – at home, at school, at work, in hospitals.

In this topic you will see how electricity helps to make our lives easier.

In this topic:

Current affairs

▶ Look at this circuit diagram:

a What does each symbol stand for?

b What happens if the circuit is not complete?

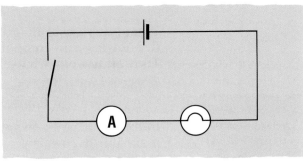

We say that the ammeter and the bulb are **in series**.
Tiny **electrons** are moving through the wires.

c Draw a circuit diagram for a battery (cell) and 2 bulbs in series.

d What can you say about the brightness of the 2 bulbs?
What can you say about the current through the 2 bulbs?
What happens if one of the bulbs breaks?

e What is an **insulator**?

f Draw a diagram of a circuit you could use to test if an object is an insulator or a conductor.

g Now draw a circuit diagram for a battery and 2 bulbs **in parallel**.

h What happens if one of the bulbs breaks?

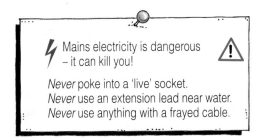

Mains electricity is dangerous
– it can kill you!

Never poke into a 'live' socket.
Never use an extension lead near water.
Never use anything with a frayed cable.

A circuit contains a battery, a switch, and 3 bulbs labelled X, Y, and Z. Bulbs X and Y are in series, and bulb Z is in parallel with X. The switch controls only bulb Z.

i Draw a circuit diagram of this.

j When all the bulbs are lit, which one is the brightest?

Investigating resistance

Connect up this circuit:

Take care to connect the ammeter the correct way round (+ of ammeter nearest to + of the battery).

k Are the components in series or in parallel?

l The current goes through only part of the variable resistor. On the diagram, is this the yellow part or the blue part?

m What happens when the slider is moved to the right on the diagram? Try it.
Why does this happen?

n If the bulb is not lit up, does it mean there must be no current in the circuit? Try it.

o Draw a circuit diagram of your circuit.

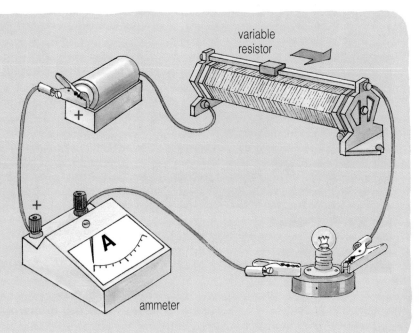

variable resistor

ammeter

Making a fire-alarm

A **bi-metallic strip** is made of 2 metals fastened together.
When it is heated, the metals get longer. They **expand**.

But one metal expands more than the other.
What happens to the strip? Try it. Explain what you see.

clamp

brass

iron

Design a fire-alarm using a bi-metallic strip.

- Think about how you can use it to ring a bell or light a warning lamp.
- Draw a circuit diagram of your design.

Ask your teacher to check your circuit. Then build it and test it.

Sketch a drawing of your fire-alarm. Describe how it works.
How could your design be improved?

You have used the bi-metallic strip as a **sensor**.

p   How could the strip be changed to make it more sensitive?

Inventing

q   Draw your fire-alarm circuit with a test button (switch) so that the bell can be tested regularly.

r   How could you change your fire-alarm design to warn you if something got too cold? Can you think of a use for this?

s   Design a circuit that will put on a heater if the room is too cold, and put on a fan if the room is too hot.
Can you do this using just one battery in the circuit?

t   Where the hot-water pipe enters a central-heating radiator, there is often a valve so you can turn off the radiator.
Design a valve that turns off the radiator when it gets hot,
. . . and turns it back on again when it cools.

Professor Messer invents a candle gadget
that gives him time to get into bed!
How does it work?

---

1   Copy and complete:

a)   If the same current goes through two bulbs, then the bulbs are in . . . .

b)   If the current splits up to go through two different paths, then we say the paths are in . . . .

c)   A good conductor has a . . . . resistance. An insulator has a . . . . resistance.

d)   An ammeter measures the . . . . in a circuit, in . . . . or A.

e)   A bi-metallic strip is made of two . . . . When it is heated, the metal that . . . . more is on the outside of the curve.

2   Draw circuit diagrams of these:

a)   A battery (cell) and a switch connected to 2 bulbs, a variable resistor and an ammeter all in series.

b)   Two batteries (cells) in series, connected to 2 bulbs wired in parallel, an ammeter to measure the total current taken by the bulbs, and a switch to control each bulb.

3   Draw a circuit diagram to show how 3 lamps can be switched on and off separately but dimmed all together.

Things to do

a List 4 things that use a battery.

b Design a circuit diagram for a torch that would let you vary the brightness.

A single **cell** like the one shown has a **voltage** of 1.5 volts. Cells that are connected together are called a battery.

c What voltage do you think you would get if you put
- two 1.5 volt cells in series?
- three 1.5 volt cells in series?

d Draw a circuit diagram that would let you test this.

A cell pushes electrons round the circuit so there is a current. A bigger voltage gives a bigger push to the electrons.

In a torch, the current *transfers energy* from the cell to the bulb. The higher the voltage, the more energy is transferred to the bulb.

The voltage across a component is also called the **potential difference** (or p.d.).

Chemical energy in a re-chargeable battery is transferred to an electric motor, where it becomes kinetic energy.

Investigating voltage

Connect up this circuit:

Take care to connect the voltmeter correctly.

e Which components are in series?

f Which components are in parallel?

g Move the slider to vary the resistance in the circuit.
Look at the voltmeter and at the bulb.
What pattern can you see?

h Leave the slider in a fixed position.
- First measure the voltage across the bulb.
- Then move the voltmeter so it is connected across the resistor.
Measure the voltage across the variable resistor.
- Then move the voltmeter again, and measure the voltage across the battery.
What do you notice about your results?

i Repeat **h** with the slider in different positions.
What pattern do you find?
Can you explain it?

j Draw a circuit diagram of the circuit shown.

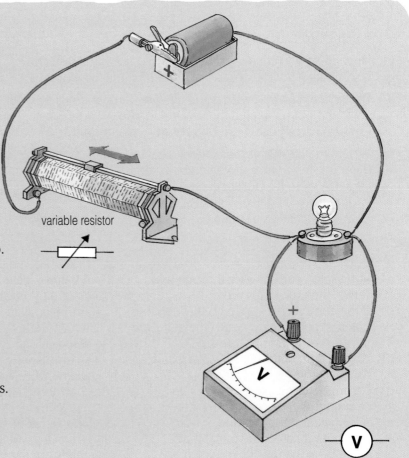

variable resistor

Energy in your home

Most of the electrical energy that you use in your home comes from the 'mains'. Mains voltage in the UK is 230 V.

k Why does this mean it is dangerous?

l How is the electricity generated?
(Hint: see lessons 21a and 21d.)

m Why does a mains plug have a fuse inside it?
How does it work?

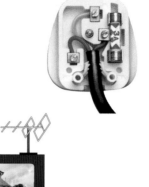

Different appliances in your home use different amounts of energy in each second. For example:
- the TV shown here transfers 100 joules in each second,
- the electric kettle transfers 2000 joules in each second.

100 W = 100 joules per second

The **rating** of each appliance is usually marked on a label (often on the back or bottom of the appliance).

For example, the electric kettle is marked 2 kW (2 kilowatts).
2 kW = 2 kilowatts = 2000 watts = 2000 joules *in each second*.
This is the amount of energy transferred from the power station to the water in the kettle.

n How many joules would the kettle transfer in 10 seconds?

2000 W = 2000 joules per second

Inside the electric kettle there is a wire with a lot of **resistance**. As the electrons are forced through this resistance, they heat it up. The electrical energy is changed ('transformed') to heat energy.

Comparing the cost

You (or your parents!) have to pay for the energy.
To run a one-bar electric fire for 1 hour costs about 8p.
It doesn't sound much, but it adds up.

And the real cost is more than 8p. It is also the effect on our environment (acid rain, global warming, loss of fossil fuels).

Your teacher will give you a Help Sheet. Use it to put some appliances in order, starting with the least expensive to run.

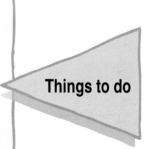

An electricity meter

---

1 Copy and complete:
a) A battery pushes .... round a circuit. The size of the push is measured in .... by using a ....
b) Two 1.5 volt cells in series can give a voltage of .... volts.
c) In a torch, the current transfers .... from the .... to the ....
The higher the voltage, the more .... is .... to the bulb.
d) In an electric kettle, the electrical .... is changed to .... energy because of the .... of the wire.

2 Draw circuit diagrams of these:
a) A cell and a switch connected to 3 bulbs in series, with a voltmeter connected across one of the bulbs.
b) A battery of 2 cells in series with a variable resistor and 2 bulbs and an ammeter. One of the bulbs has a voltmeter across it.
c) A cell in parallel with 2 bulbs. One of the bulbs is controlled by a switch. The other bulb is controlled by a variable resistor and this bulb has a voltmeter across it.

Things to do

In lesson 24a you made a fire-alarm system.
It was made from several components.
You joined them together to make a **system**, to do a job.

All systems are made up of 3 basic parts:

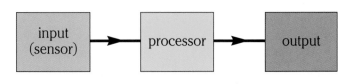

For your fire-alarm,
The **input** was the heat which made the bi-metallic strip bend. The bi-metallic strip is a **sensor**.

The **processor** was the circuit which was completed by the contact.

The **output** was a bell ringing (or a bulb lighting up).

Here is another system, a radio:
The input is the radio signal coming into the aerial.
The processor is the amplifier inside the case.
The output is the sound coming out of the loudspeakers.

▶ Write down   i) the input and   ii) the output,
for each of these systems:

a a door-bell
b a coffee-machine
c your calculator
d putting your hand in hot water!

Electronic systems are now very common.
▶ Read this short story:

Lisa saw a fan-club advertised on **teletext** but she lost part of the address. So she used a **computer** to search for the address in a **database**. She used a **search engine** on the **internet**. Then she wrote a letter to the fan-club using a **word-processor**. She checked it on the **VDU** and stored it on **disc**. Then she sent her letter by **e-mail**, using a **modem**. The fan-club sent her a membership form by **fax**.

e Explain each of the bold words, in as much detail as you can.

In your group, discuss the effects of this new technology.
• How has it changed life over the last 20 years?
• What are its advantages and disadvantages?
• How do you think electronics will change life over the next 20 years?

Analogue or digital?

The hands on a clock are always on the move. They move on a continuous scale round the dial. This is an **analogue** system.

In a **digital** clock, the time is shown in steps. It is only changed every minute.

f Look at these photos, and decide which things are analogue and which are digital.

g What are the advantages and the disadvantages of these 2 methods of display?

Electronic systems are often digital systems. They often have only 2 states: OFF and ON. For example, your fire-alarm had only 2 states: it was OFF or ON. A light switch is either OFF or ON.

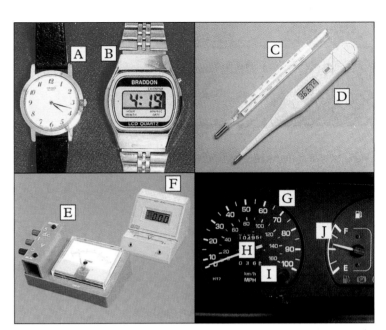

Binary logic

A system with only 2 states is also called a binary system.
When it is OFF it has a binary code of **0** (zero).
When it is ON it has a binary code of **1**.
These are also called **logic 0** and **logic 1**.

▶ Copy this table and complete it:

Binary code	Switch	Lamp	Bell	Current flowing	Answer to a question	Logic
1		ON			YES	**1**
0	OFF		silent	NO		**0**

Sending signals

The Morse Code is made up of dots and dashes:

h Is it an analogue or a digital signal?

i Draw a circuit diagram of a system to send and receive Morse Code from someone in another room.

j Write a message in Morse Code and send it to a friend. Can they de-code it correctly?

A ● —	J ● — — —
B — ● ● ●	K — ● —
C — ● — ●	L ● — ● ●
D — ● ●	M — —
E ●	N — ●
F ● ● — ●	O — — —
G — — ●	P ● — — ●
H ● ● ● ●	Q — — ● —
I ● ●	R ● — ●
S ● ● ●	
T —	
U ● ● —	
V ● ● ● —	
W ● — —	
X — ● ● —	
Y — ● — —	
Z — — ● ●	

Things to do

1 Copy and complete:
a) All systems have . . . . basic parts: input, ... , and . . . .
b) An . . . . signal can have a continuous range of values. A signal which can be only ON or OFF is called a . . . . signal.

2 Are you in favour of video-phones? Write a short story about a home of the future that uses a lot of new technology.

3 Write down i) the input and ii) the output, for each of these systems:
a) a burglar alarm b) an electric guitar
c) a torch d) automatic doors in a shop
e) a TV set f) you hearing your name.

4 Are these analogue or digital?
a) the volume control on a radio
b) traffic lights
c) the school bell.

Sensors

24d

Your eye is a **sensor**. It detects light and gives an input to your system.

a What other sensors do you have in your body?

In your fire-alarm, the sensor was the bi-metallic strip. It detected a change in temperature.

Here are some more sensors:

Movement

A **micro-switch** starts and stops a current.
It senses the movement and produces an electrical signal.

A **tilt switch** contains 2 wires and a blob of mercury, as shown. Mercury is a liquid, and a conductor.

b What can happen if this switch is tilted?

c Design a burglar alarm that will go off if a desk lid or a car bonnet is lifted up. Draw a circuit diagram.

d Where else could you use a tilt switch sensor?

Magnetism

A **reed switch** is a magnetic switch. It detects when a magnet comes near.
See the experiment on the opposite page.

Moisture

A **moisture sensor** has 2 wires close together but not touching. If a rain-drop lands so that it touches both wires, a current can flow. This is because rain-water is a conductor.

e Who might want a moisture detector?

Sound

A **microphone** detects sound and makes an electrical signal.

Light

A **light-dependent resistor** is called an **LDR**.
See the investigation on the opposite page.

f Where would a light sensor be useful?

Temperature

A **thermistor** is a useful temperature sensor.
See the investigation on the opposite page.

g Where would a temperature sensor be useful?

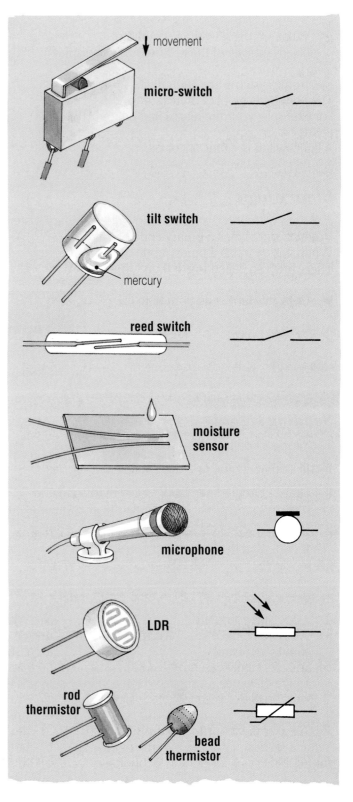

Looking at a reed switch

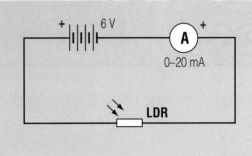

reed switch

- What happens as you bring the magnet near? At what distance does this happen?
- Use a magnifying glass to look closely at it.
- Devise a burglar alarm for a window, using a reed switch.

Investigating an LDR *(light-dependent resistor)*

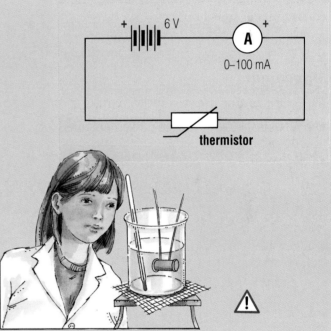

- What happens as you vary the amount of light on the LDR?
- When does most current flow? When does the LDR have least resistance to the current?
- How does the current depend on the colour of the light? Which colour is best?

Investigating a thermistor

Use this circuit to investigate how the **current** depends on the **temperature** of the thermistor.

- How many readings will you take?
- How will you record your results?
- How can you make your results more reliable?

- What pattern do you find?
- When does the thermistor pass the most current? When does it have the least resistance?

- Design a thermometer for a car. It should show the driver the temperature of the engine.

- If you have time, plot a graph of your results.

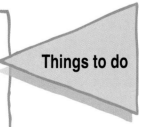

Things to do

1 Copy and complete:
a) A reed switch is a . . . . switch. It is switched on when a . . . . comes near to it.
b) An LDR is a . . . . -dependent . . . . The brighter the . . . . that shines on it, the more . . . . can flow through it.
c) A thermistor is a . . . . sensor. The hotter it is, the more . . . . can flow through it.

2 Make a list of the electronic sensors that you have in your home.

3 Suggest a sensor for each system:
a) To tell you if it is raining outside.
b) To tell you if the baby upstairs cries.
c) To tell a pilot that he is taking off too steeply.
d) To tell a blind person that it is time to close the curtains at night.

Outputs

a Every system has 3 parts. What are they**?**

b If you pick up a very hot object, what is your output signal**?**

c What was the output from the fire-alarm that you made**?**

This page tells you about some of the **output** devices that you can use in electronic systems.

Light

You have already used filament lamps in your circuits.

LED lights are often used in electronics.
LED stands for **l**ight-**e**mitting **d**iode.
LEDs are usually red or green. They use much less current than filament bulbs.

d Where have you seen LEDs used**?**

Movement

An electric **motor** uses electricity to make movement.

e What is the name for the movement energy in a motor**?**

f Make a list of the motors in your home.

Sound

A sound can be made by a bell, a buzzer, or a loudspeaker.

g When do you use a loudspeaker**?**

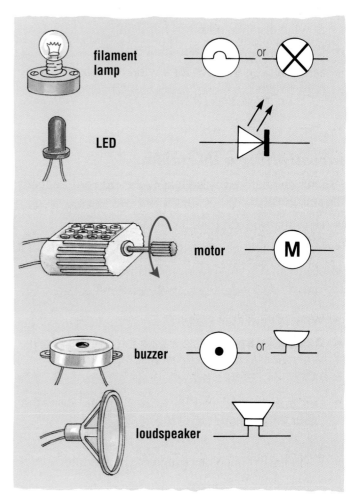

Using a relay

In some circuits, we might want to use a small current to switch on a larger current.

We can do this by using a **relay**. It contains an electromagnet.
Look carefully at this diagram:

There are 2 circuits here.

h When a small current flows in the blue circuit, what happens to the iron core**?**

i How does this change the red circuit**?**

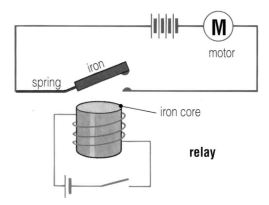

Making connections

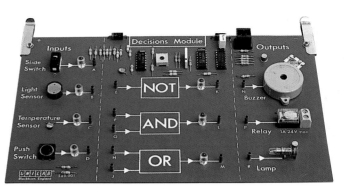

Use an electronics kit to investigate inputs and outputs. If the kit is like the one shown here, try to ignore the middle part of the board for now.

▶ Look at each of the inputs.

An input is ON when its red LED lights. This is also called logic **1**.
Find out how to make each input go ON and OFF.

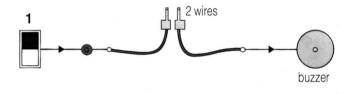

▶ Connect a wire from the **slide switch** to the **lamp**:
How do you make the lamp go ON and OFF?

Now try each of the sensors with the lamp.
And then with the buzzer.

Look closely at the **relay** while you switch it ON and OFF.
What do you see?
How can you use the relay to switch a motor ON and OFF?

▶ You can make a **moisture sensor** like this:

What happens when you connect the 2 wires with a damp cloth?
You could use this as a wet-nappy detector!

Now design circuits for **j** to **p**.
Test each design, and then draw a labelled diagram of it.
The first one has been done for you.

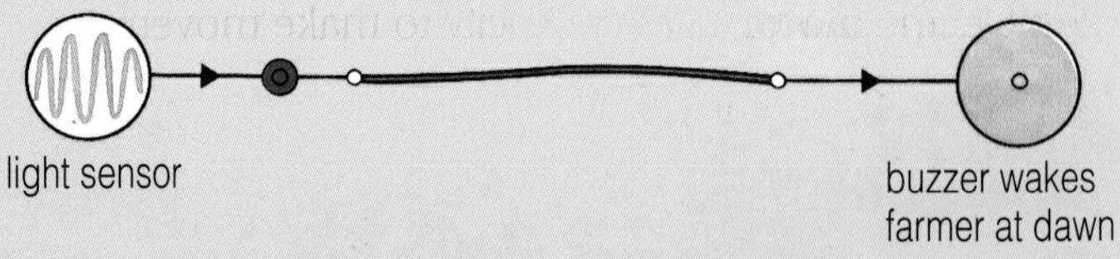

light sensor

buzzer wakes
farmer at dawn

j An alarm to wake up a farmer at dawn:

k A fire-alarm for a blind person.

l A burglar alarm using a pressure pad.

m A burglar alarm for a drawer.
(Hint: it is usually dark inside a drawer.)

n A hot-breath detector:

o To switch on a fan when the room gets too hot. If possible, connect a motor and a battery to your relay.

p To tell a blind person when to stop pouring from a tea-pot.

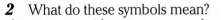

1 Copy and complete:
a) LED stands for:
b) In a relay, a small . . . . can switch on a large . . . .

2 What do these symbols mean?
a)   b)   c)

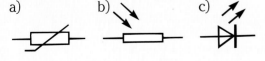

3 Draw a connection diagram (like the ones above) for each of these:
a) An alarm if a chip-pan gets too hot.
b) An alarm that detects a burglar's torch.
c) To tell you if it is raining outside.
d) To open a greenhouse window if it gets too hot.
e) To switch on a water-pump if a ditch fills with water.
f) To call a nurse if a patient's temperature is too high.

Things to do

Making decisions

A system has 3 parts. Can you remember what they are?

The middle part of a system is often a **logic gate**. It is an electronic 'chip' that can make decisions.

Logic gates act rather like doors or garden gates. They only let you through if you open them in the correct way.

NOT gate

Connect a push switch directly to a buzzer: What happens?

Now include a NOT gate, like this: What difference does it make?

Do the same with the other input sensors.

How can you make the buzzer come on when it is **NOT** warm? (It is cold.)

Then when it is **NOT** light? (It is dark.)

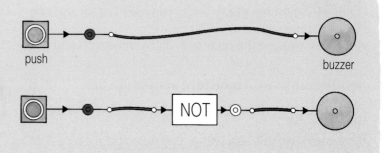

The output signal is **NOT** the same as the input signal.

AND gate

Connect a slide switch and a push switch to the AND gate, like this:

What do you have to do to get the buzzer to sound?

What do you notice about the red LEDs?
Remember: ON is a logical **1**, OFF is a logical **0**.

How can you make the buzzer come on when it is light **AND** warm?

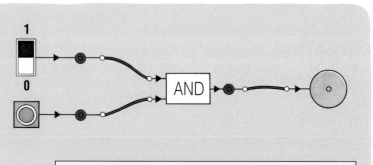

The output signal is **1** (ON) only if:
the first input is **1**   **AND**   the second input is **1**.

OR gate

An OR gate opens in a different way from the other gates.
Connect the OR gate like this:

What are the rules to make the buzzer work now?

How can you make the buzzer come on when it is warm **OR** the push switch is pressed?

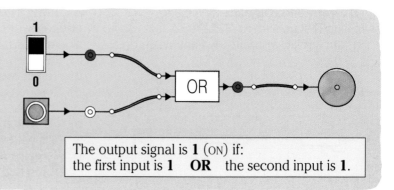

The output signal is **1** (ON) if:
the first input is **1**   **OR**   the second input is **1**.

Solving problems

Problem: Baby Jane is in an incubator. It is very important that the nurse is warned if the baby gets cold. Can you help?

Solution: Warm up your thermistor with your finger and make this system:

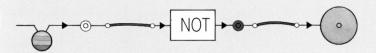

What happens when the thermistor cools down?
In the hospital, where would you put each part of the system?

Problem: Mr Smith likes to go to bed early, and doesn't want his doorbell ringing at night. Can you help?

Solution: Try this system:

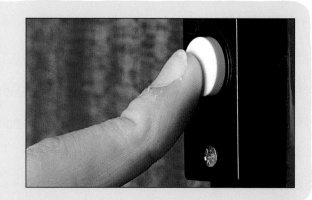

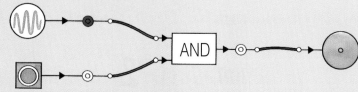

What happens at night? Why?
The system is making the decision for you.

Problem: Jenny is designing a new push-chair.
Her idea is that a buzzer will warn you if you let go of the handle (a push switch) without putting on the foot-brake first (a slide switch). Can you help?

Solution: You'll need 2 gates for this:

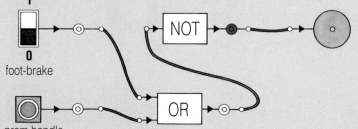

What happens if the foot-brake is off (logical 0) and you let go of the handle switch? Why?

---

1 Copy and complete:
a) NOT, AND and OR are three . . . . gates.
b) In a NOT gate, the output is . . . . the same as the input signal.
c) In an AND gate, the output is ON (logical **1**) only if the first input is **1** . . . . the second input is **1**.
d) In an OR gate, the output is **1** (ON) if the first input is **1** . . . . the second input is **1**.

2 Draw system diagrams (like the ones above) to solve these problems:
a) To switch on a street-light when the sky goes dark.
b) To open the window of a greenhouse if it is warm **and** it is day-time. (You can use a relay to switch on a motor.)
c) To sound an alarm if the temperature in a freezer gets too high **or** if the door is left open (so that light is shining in).

Things to do

Questions

1 The diagram shows a circuit with two 2-way switches.
Wire C can be connected to either A or B.
This circuit is often used for the lighting on a staircase.
   a) In the diagram, is the lamp on or off?
   b) Describe carefully how the circuit works, using the letters on the diagram in your answer.
   c) What are the advantages of this circuit?

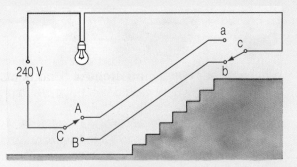

2 Keung and Donna are talking about batteries.
They each have a hypothesis:
Keung says, "The HP2 cell is larger and so it will make the bulb brighter."
Donna says, "The HP7 cell will make the bulb just as bright but the cell won't last as long."
   a) Who do you think is right?
   b) Plan an investigation to find out who is right.

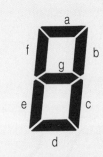

3 Look at the display on your calculator.
   a) Why is it called a seven-segment display?
   b) Why is it called a digital display?
   c) If only segments a, b, c are ON, what number is displayed?
   d) Using logic 1 = segment ON, this could be written in code as 1110000. What number would be displayed if the code is 1101101?
   e) Write down the code to display a number 5.

4 a) The warden of a nature reserve wants an alarm that will warn her if anyone goes near the nest of a rare bird. Design a system to do this, making it as fool-proof as possible.
   b) Then she asks for a way to monitor the temperature of the bird's eggs from her office. Draw a circuit diagram for her.

5 a) A laundry needs an alarm to warn if the hot-water tank starts to cool down during the day. Design a system for this and include a test switch.
   b) Design a system to warn you when the soil of your house-plant becomes dry. You wouldn't want it to warn you during the night.

Plants at work

25

Can you imagine what life would be like without plants?

We use plants for food, fuel, building materials and medicines. Plants also take waste carbon dioxide out of the air and make oxygen for us to breathe.

In this topic:

The great energy trap

Plants can't eat like animals do.
So how do they get their food?

▶ Write down some ideas about how you think plants feed.

Plants make their food from simple substances.
But to do this they need energy.
Where do you think this energy comes from?
What part of the plant do you think traps this energy?

Plants make food by the process of **photosynthesis** (photo = light *and* synthesis = to make). To make food they need:

- carbon dioxide from the air
- water from the soil
- light energy trapped by **chlorophyll**.

$$\text{CARBON DIOXIDE} + \text{WATER} \xrightarrow[\text{CHLOROPHYLL}]{\text{SUNLIGHT}} \text{SUGAR} + \text{OXYGEN}$$

▶ Write down the answers to these questions:

a What food do plants make themselves?

b Which gas is made during photosynthesis?

c How do animals use this gas?

Oxygen bubbles

Jill and Emma had seen fish tanks with air bubblers. They knew that these were to put oxygen into the water for the fish to breathe. Jill read that if there is lots of pondweed and the tank is well lit, air bubblers aren't needed.

Jill and Emma set up an investigation to see the effect of light on the pondweed.
They put some pondweed in a test-tube of pond water.
They placed a lamp at different distances from the test-tube and counted the number of bubbles of gas produced in a minute.

Their results are shown in the table:

Distance of lamp from pondweed (cm)	10	20	40	Lamp off
Number of bubbles produced per minute	15	7	4	2

d Which gas do you think was produced by the pondweed?

e How could you prove this?

f Do you think there is a pattern to these results?

g Emma thought that the lamp might also warm up the pondweed and not make it a fair test. How could you improve the design of their investigation to avoid this?

Testing a leaf for starch

Most of the sugar made in the leaves of a plant is changed to starch.
You can test for this starch with iodine.
If the leaf turns blue-black with iodine then starch has been made.

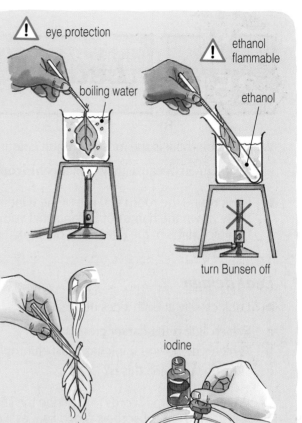

eye protection

boiling water

ethanol
flammable

ethanol

turn Bunsen off

- Dip a leaf into boiling water for about 1 minute to soften it.

- Turn off the Bunsen burner.

- Put the leaf into a test-tube of ethanol. Stand the test-tube in the hot water for about 10 minutes.

- Wash the leaf in cold water.

- Spread the leaf out flat on a petri dish and cover it with iodine. What colour does the leaf go?

h Why was it important that you turn off the Bunsen burner when you were heating the ethanol?

i What was the leaf like after you heated it in the ethanol?

j Was there any starch in the leaf that you tested?

k Plants make new **biomass** during photosynthesis. What is meant by biomass?

iodine

Stripes and patches

Not all leaves are green all over.
Some have white and green patches, others stripes.
If you have time, try testing one of these leaves for starch.

l Which parts do you think will go blue-black?

Remember to draw a picture of what your leaf looks like at the start to show which parts are green.

---

1 Copy and complete:
Plants make their food by . . . . They use . . . .
. . . . from the air and . . . . from the soil. They also need a green substance called . . . . which traps . . . . energy. The food that is made is sugar and it is changed to . . . . in the leaf. The waste gas made is called . . . .

2 Plants are important because they provide:
a) food
b) fuel
c) building materials
d) medicines.
Find examples of plants that provide each of these things.

3 Explain why a) and b) are vital to our survival.
a) Plants use up carbon dioxide.
b) Plants release oxygen.

4 Joseph Priestley found that a lighted candle in a jar soon went out. He put a plant in the jar and shone light on it for a week. He found the lighted candle now burned much longer. Can you explain his experiment?

Things to do

Leaves

What do you think is the most common colour in nature?

Plants are green because they contain **chlorophyll**.

▶ Look round the room and out of the window.
Write down the names of 5 plants that you see.
In which parts of the plants do you think there is most chlorophyll?

Leaf design

▶ Look closely at both sides of a leaf.

a Which side is the darker green?

b Which side do you think has most chlorophyll?

c Why do you think this is?

▶ Write down some words to describe the shape of your leaf.
A leaf's job is to absorb as much light as it can.
How do you think its shape helps it to do this?

Looking inside a leaf

Look at a section of a leaf under your microscope.
Focus onto the leaf at low power.
Now carefully change the magnification to high power.
Can you see any of the parts labelled in the diagram on your slide?

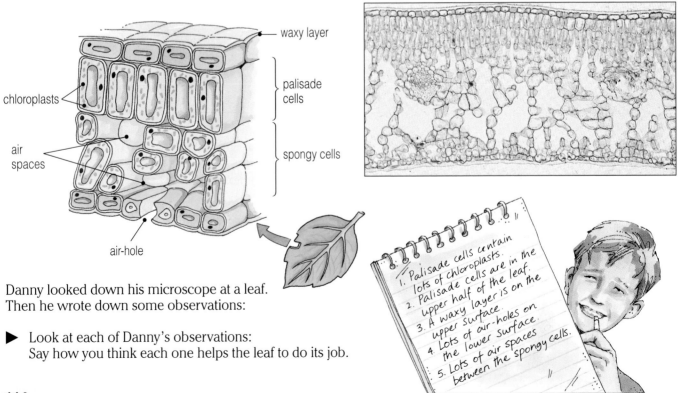

Danny looked down his microscope at a leaf.
Then he wrote down some observations:

▶ Look at each of Danny's observations:
Say how you think each one helps the leaf to do its job.

1. Palisade cells contain lots of chloroplasts.
2. Palisade cells are in the upper half of the leaf.
3. A waxy layer is on the upper surface.
4. Lots of air-holes on the lower surface.
5. Lots of air spaces between the spongy cells.

Holey leaves

Try dropping a leaf into a beaker of boiling water.
Which surface do bubbles appear from?
Why do you think this is?

eye protection

Gases from the air pass into and out of a leaf through **air-holes**.

Paint a small square (1 cm × 1 cm) on the underside of a leaf with nail varnish.
The nail varnish will make an imprint of the leaf surface.

Wait for it to dry completely.
(While you are waiting, you can set up your microscope.)
Carefully peel off the nail varnish with some tweezers.
Put it on a slide with a drop of water and a coverslip.
Observe and draw 2 or 3 air-holes at high power.
Repeat for the upper surface of your leaf.

Write down your conclusions.

Respiration in plants

All living things carry out respiration to get energy, and that includes plants. Can you remember the equation for respiration?

SUGAR + OXYGEN → CARBON DIOXIDE + WATER + ENERGY

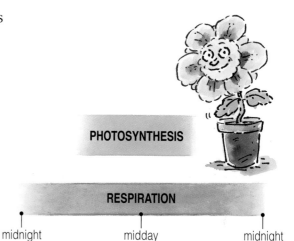

d During respiration, how do you think oxygen gets into the plant and carbon dioxide gets out?

e During photosynthesis: i) which gas passes into a leaf? and
ii) which gas passes out of a leaf?

Some people think that plants carry out photosynthesis during the day and respiration at night. This is wrong.

f Look at the diagram and say what really happens.

As you can see plants carry out respiration **all the time** and carry out photosynthesis only **in the light**.

PHOTOSYNTHESIS

RESPIRATION

midnight   midday   midnight

Things to do

1 Match each of the leaf parts on the left with the job that they do on the right:

air-holes carry water up from stem
palisade cells allow gases to pass into and out of leaf
spongy cells contain many chloroplasts
waxy layer contain many air spaces
veins prevents too much water being lost

2 Do plants of the same species always have the same leaf area?
Plan an investigation to compare the leaf area of the same plants found in light and shady conditions. Try to explain any differences that you find.

3 Leaves have a large surface area to absorb light. Lay a leaf onto graph paper, draw around it and work out its area by counting the squares. Can you work out the total leaf area of the plant?

4 Leaves are thin so gases can get in and out easily. But they can also lose water and then they droop.
Look closely at a leaf and say what helps to stop them from drooping.

Pollination

Many people give flowers to friends and relatives.
But how many realise that flowers are a plant's reproductive system?

Flowers have male and female reproductive organs.
The male parts produce the male sex cells.
The female parts produce the female sex cells.

▶ Write down some words to describe what flowers are like.

A closer look

You can use a hand-lens to look at your flower in more detail.
Cut the flower in half like the one in the picture.
See if you can find all the parts labelled in the picture.

Many flowers have male and female parts.
The female parts are called the **carpels**.
Look at the picture:

a What is each carpel made up of?

The male parts are called the **stamens**.

b What is each stamen made up of?

Use a hand-lens to look closely at these parts in your flower.

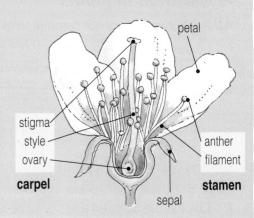

Make a flower poster

Take a new flower and carefully remove all the parts with tweezers.
Start on the outside with the sepals. Then work inwards removing the petals, stamens and carpels.
Arrange the parts in a line, one under the other, in your book.
Stick them down neatly with sellotape and label the parts.
Your teacher can give you a Help Sheet that shows you how to do this.

Male and female cells

The stamens are the male parts of a flower.
Each stamen is an **anther** and a **filament** (or stalk).
The male sex cells are made inside the anthers.
Each male sex cell is called a **pollen grain**.

The carpels are the female parts of a flower.
Each carpel is made up of a **stigma**, a **style** and an **ovary**.
The female sex cells are made inside the ovary.
Each female sex cell is called an **ovule**.

If fertilisation is to take place, a pollen grain and an ovule must join together.

c How do you think the pollen grains reach the ovules?
Write down your ideas.

Can you see the ovary in this flower?

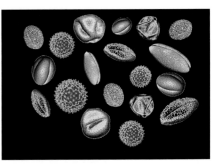

Different pollen grains

Carried by insects

Pollination is the transfer of pollen from the anthers of a flower to the stigma.

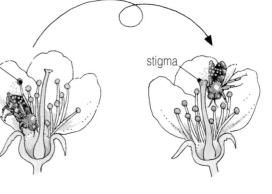

anther

stigma

d At what time of year are most flowers out?

e At what time of year are insects such as bees and butterflies out?

Insects are a great help in carrying pollen from one flower to another.
But first, the flowers have to attract the insects to them.

f Write down 3 ways in which flowers can attract insects.

▶ Look at the picture showing **insect pollination**.

g Why do you think the bee reaches down into the first flower?

h How does the bee carry pollen to the second flower?

i Where does the bee leave pollen in the second flower?

Blown by the wind

Not all flowers need insects to pollinate them.
Many flowers like grasses and cereals rely on the wind to carry their pollen to another flower.

▶ Look at a wind-pollinated flower with a hand-lens.

j How does it compare with your insect-pollinated flower?
  • Is it brightly coloured?
  • Does it have a scent?
  • Does it have **nectar**?

k Why do you think this is?

l What do you think its pollen is like?
  • Is the pollen sticky?
  • Is it light or heavy?
  • Is much pollen produced?

m Why do you think this is?

▶ Make a table to show all the differences that you have found out between insect-pollinated flowers and wind-pollinated flowers.

---

1 Copy and complete:
The male parts of a flower are called the . . . . and are made up of 2 parts: the . . . . and the . . . . The female parts of a flower are called the . . . . and are made up of the . . . . , the . . . . and the . . . . Pollination is the transfer of . . . . from the anthers of one flower to the . . . . of another.

2 **Cross-pollination** is when pollen is transferred to separate flowers. What do you think is meant by **self-pollination**? How could it take place?

3 Did you know that 1 in 10 people suffer from **hay fever**?
Find out what the symptoms are.
When do you think people suffer most?
Find out what the **pollen count** is and what sort of weather conditons can affect it.

4 Copy and complete these half-sentences:
a) Some flowers attract insects because they have . . . .
b) Wind-pollinated flowers do not need colour because . . . .
c) Insect-pollinated flowers have sticky pollen because . . . .
d) Wind-pollinated flowers make lots of pollen because . . . .

Things to do

Making seeds

Most new plants grow from **seeds**.
But where do you think seeds come from?
How are seeds formed?

▶ Write down some of your ideas.

Seeds are formed when a male sex cell joins with a female sex cell.

Fertilisation

Inside each pollen grain is a male **pollen nucleus**.
Inside each ovule is a female **ovule nucleus**.

a What do we call the joining together of a male nucleus and a female nucleus?

Once it is fertilised, the ovule grows into a seed.

▶ Look at the pictures to see how fertilisation takes place in a flowering plant:

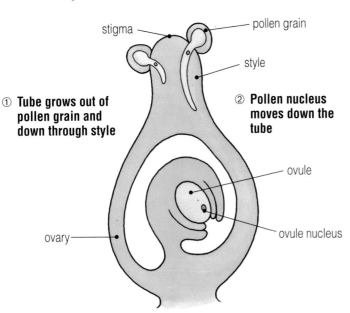

stigma
pollen grain
style

① **Tube grows out of pollen grain and down through style**

② **Pollen nucleus moves down the tube**

ovule

ovary

ovule nucleus

③ **Pollen nucleus joins with ovule nucleus. Fertilisation takes place and a seed will form.**

b Where do you think the pollen grain comes from?

c What happens to a pollen grain after it lands on a stigma?

d How does the pollen nucleus reach the ovule nucleus?

After fertilisation, most parts of the flower, wither and die.
The ovary gets bigger and forms the **fruit**. Inside the fruit are the seeds.

e What do you think the fruits and seeds are like in these plants:
  i) grape?   ii) oak tree?   iii) pea?   iv) tomato?

If a new plant is to survive and grow well its seed must first be carried away from the parent plant.
Seeds are often scattered over a wide area.

f Why do you think this is important?

g Write down some different ways in which seeds can be scattered.

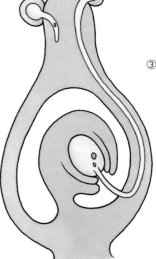

Pea and pod seeds

Half a tomato fruit: can you see the seeds?

Seed fall

"Seeds that fall slowly have a better chance of being carried further by the wind" said the man in the gardening programme.
Do you think that this is true?

Plan an investigation to find out how slowly different seeds fall.

- Think carefully about what apparatus you will need.
- What measurements are you going to make?
- Remember to make it a fair test.

Show your plan to your teacher, then try it out.

Seeds and babies

How does fertilisation in flowering plants compare with fertilisation in humans?
Copy and complete the table:

	Flowering plant	Human
Name of male sex cell		
Name of female sex cell		
Place where male sex cells are made		
Place where female sex cells are made		
How does the male sex cell reach the female sex cell?		
What is formed after fertilisation?		

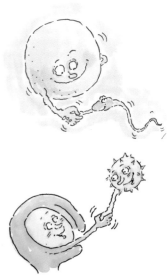

▶ Write down the ways in which the male and female sex cells in a human are different from those in flowering plants.

---

1 Write out the following sentences in the correct order to describe how plants reproduce:
A   Pollen nucleus joins with ovule nucleus.
B   Pollen grain lands on stigma.
C   The fertilised ovule becomes a seed.
D   The pollen grain grows into a pollen tube.
E   The pollen nucleus travels down the pollen tube to the ovule.

2   What do we mean by fertilisation?
In a flowering plant, what takes the place of:
a)   the sperm?   b)   the egg?
c)   the fertilised egg?

3   What happens to each of the following after fertilisation:
a)   the flower?   b)   the ovule?
c)   the ovary?

4   a)   Why don't seeds germinate (grow) in a gardening shop?
b)   What do they need to grow?
c)   Copy the drawing of a germinating seed and label it using these words:

new leaves   seed coat   new root
new shoot   food store

Things to do

Questions

1 Label the parts of the leaf using the following words:
palisade cells, air spaces, epidermis, air-holes, waxy layer,
spongy cells, chloroplasts.
Write down: A = chloroplasts, etc.

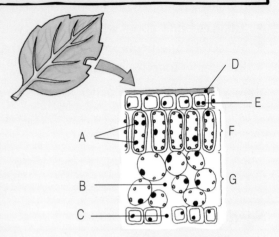

2 Sanjit shone different amounts of light on some pondweed.
He recorded the number of bubbles of gas given off by the
pondweed per minute:

Units of light	Number of bubbles per minute
1	6
2	14
3	21
4	24
5	26
6	27
7	27

a) Draw a line-graph to display his results.
b) How many bubbles of gas would you expect the plant to make at
  i) 2.5 units of light?   ii) 8 units of light?

3 Stems grow up and roots grow down.
But does it matter which way up a seed is planted in the soil?
Plan an investigation to find out.

4 a) Why do you think that woodland plants like primroses and
  wood anemones flower in the spring?
b) Why do you think hazel 'catkins' make lots of pollen?
c) Why do you think it is important that seeds get far away from
  the parent plant?

5 The flowers of some plants are brightly coloured and contain nectar.
a) Why are these things important for pollination?
b) Why don't all plants have brightly coloured flowers containing
  nectar?
c) On which part of the flower does pollen form?
d) On which part of the flower is pollen deposited during
  pollination?

6 Here are 4 ways in which seeds may be dispersed from the parent
plant. Describe each method of dispersal and give an example of a
plant that uses it.
a) Inside an animal.
b) On an animal.
c) On the wind.
d) By dehiscing ('exploding').

Sight and Sound

26

We use our eyes and ears all the time.

We need them to make sense of the world around us.

Light waves and sound waves are useful to us in many other ways as well, as you will see and hear . . .

Reflection and refraction

▶ Kate is looking into a **plane** mirror.
A ray of light from the lamp is *reflected* from the mirror:

a Which is the incident ray? Which is the reflected ray?

b If the angle of incidence is 20°, how big is the angle of reflection?

c Explain why Kate sees the lamp.

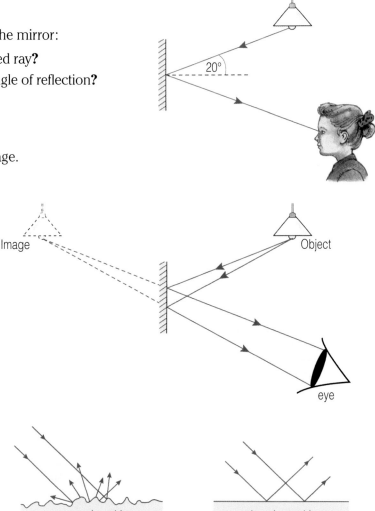

▶ Kate sees an **image** of the lamp. It is called a *virtual* image – you cannot touch a virtual image.

d Write down the word IMAGE as it would look when seen in a mirror.

▶ Here is another diagram of Kate looking at the lamp:

It shows 2 rays from the lamp going into Kate's eye.
When Kate looks at the mirror, she sees the image **behind** the mirror.
The image is *where the rays appear to come from*.

e If the lamp is 2 metres from the mirror, where exactly does Kate see the image?

▶ This diagram shows a beam of light being *scattered* from a piece of paper:

f Why can't you see an image in a sheet of paper?

paper (rough)   mirror (smooth)

MIRROR ЯOЯЯIM

Your teacher may give you a Help Sheet with these diagrams:

Tina likes to go to pop concerts, but often she can't see over the crowd.
How can she use mirrors to see the band?

Mr Brown wants to see all the shelves in his shop, in case of shop-lifters.
How can he use a mirror (or 2 mirrors) to see his shelves?

Refraction

▶ The diagram shows a ray of light going into a glass block:

g What happens to the ray when it enters the glass?
This is called **refraction**.
On the diagram you can see a blue dotted line labelled **N**.
This is called the **normal** line.

h Is the light ray bent away from or towards the normal?

i Which is bigger – the angle of incidence (**i**) or the angle of refraction (**r**)?

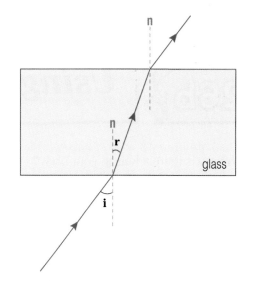

Light travels very fast in air – at 300 000 km per second!
In glass it travels more slowly. As the light is slowed down, it is refracted towards the normal.

j What happens to the light ray as it leaves the glass?

Lenses

▶ The diagram shows 2 lenses:

k One of them is a **converging** lens and one is a **diverging** lens. Which is which?

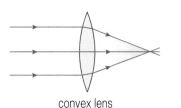

convex lens   concave lens

Investigating lenses

Your teacher will give you 3 convex lenses (thick, medium, and thin).

• Use each lens as a magnifying glass to look at your finger:

• Which lens magnifies the most? Which least? Is there a pattern?

• What happens if you use 2 lenses together?

• Use them to look at a photo in this book. What do you see?

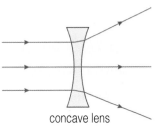

1 Copy and complete:
a) When light is reflected, the angle of .... is .... to the angle of ....
b) The distance from an object to a plane mirror is .... to the distance from the .... to the mirror.
c) When light goes into glass, it is .... towards the normal line.
When light comes out of glass, it is refracted .... from the normal.
d) In a convex lens, the .... come closer together. It is a .... lens.
e) A concave lens is a .... lens.
f) A fat convex lens is a strong .... glass.

2 Think about all the ways that mirrors are used – in homes, shops, and cars. Make a list of all the uses that you can think of, in 2 columns: (1) plane mirrors, (2) curved mirrors.

3 Dave's imagic trick. (Try it!)
The diagram shows Amy looking at a cup:
She cannot see the coin lying in the cup.
Dave pours some water into the cup. Now Amy can see the coin!
Why? Can you explain it by drawing a ray diagram?

Things to do

Using light

▶ Where is there a lens in your body?
Is it convex or concave?
Does it converge or diverge rays of light?

▶ Sketch a simple diagram of an eye, like the one shown
(or your teacher may give you a Help Sheet).
Then add these labels in the right places:

lens   retina   iris   pupil   cornea

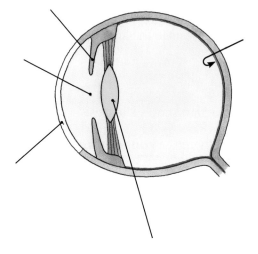

a You are using your eyes to see this page.
Explain, step by step, how the light travels from the
window until it is focussed on your retina.
You can start like this:

Light from the window shines on the book, and then...

b What happens to the pupil in your eye if you look at a
bright light?

Focussing your eyes

The lens in your eye can change shape. When you look at
near objects it gets fatter. For far objects it gets thinner.
The muscles in your eye make the lens go fatter or thinner,
until the image is sharp:

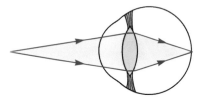

Looking at a near object, your lens is **fat**.

If you can't see a near object clearly, you are long-sighted.
(You may need spectacles with con<u>vex</u> lenses.)

Looking at a far object, your lens is **thin**.

If you can't see a distant object clearly, you are short-sighted.
(You may need spectacles with con<u>cave</u> lenses.)

Eye tests

Plan, and carry out, an investigation to find out the distances
at which you can read letters of different sizes.

• How will you make it a fair test?

• Is it the same for the left eye, the right eye, and both eyes?

• Plot a graph of the ***distance from your eye*** against the
size of the letter. What do you find?

• Is your graph the same as other people's?

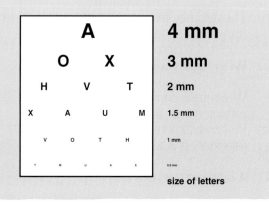

The camera

In a camera, a lens is used to make an image on the film:

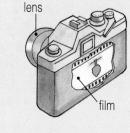

Use a convex lens to focus the light rays from a lamp, like in a camera:

- What do you notice about the image?
- Move the lamp to different distances from the screen. Each time, focus the image. Measure the distances shown on the diagram, and record them in a table.
- What pattern do you find?

- In a camera, how do you focus on
  - near objects?
  - far objects?

- Does your eye focus on objects in this way?

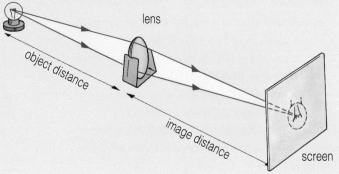

▶ Look at this diagram of a camera:

c Which part of the camera is like your retina?

The **aperture** can be changed to let in more or less light.

open   closed

d Which part of your eye is like this?

e When should the camera use a small aperture?

f In what other way can a camera change the amount of light going to the film?

g The camera and your eye both use a lens. In what ways are the lenses i) similar? and ii) different?

h Explain carefully how your eye and a camera use different ways to focus the image.

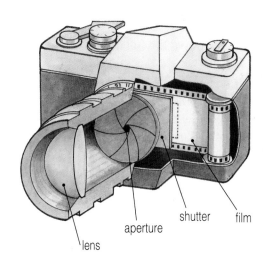

---

1 Copy and complete:
a) My eye lens is a . . . . lens. It . . . . the rays of light.
b) To focus on near and far objects, my eye . . . . changes shape. To focus on . . . . objects, it is fatter.
c) A long-sighted person cannot focus on . . . . objects. A short-sighted person cannot focus on . . . . objects.
d) The . . . . in a camera and in my eye are inverted (upside-down).

2 Copy and complete:
a) A camera uses a . . . . lens.
b) To focus a camera on near objects, the lens is moved . . . . from the film.
c) The . . . . in a camera is like the iris in my eye.

3 Draw up a table or a poster which shows all the ways in which a camera and your eye are i) similar, and ii) different.

Things to do

A world of colour

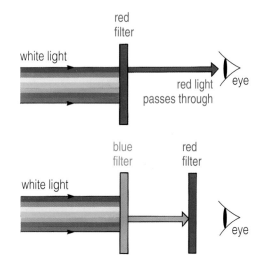

▶ Which is your favourite colour?
What does it remind you of?

a How many colours are there in a rainbow?

b How can you remember their names?

Making a spectrum

You can make a **spectrum** using a prism:

c When the light enters the prism it is **refracted**. Is it refracted towards the normal or away from the normal?

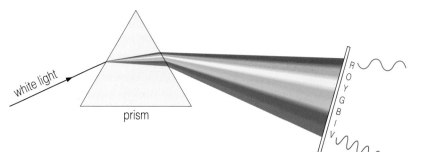

The white light is **dispersed** by the prism, to make a spectrum.
This shows that white light is really a mixture of seven colours.

d Write down the full names of the 7 colours, in order.

e Red light has the longest wavelength. Which colour has the shortest?

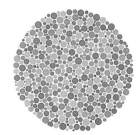

The light is refracted because it travels slower in the glass than in the air.
Different colours travel at different speeds, and so are refracted by different amounts.

f Which colour do you think travels slowest in glass?

Can you see a red number here?
If you can't, you may be colour-blind.

Filters

What do you see when you look through a piece of red plastic or red glass?
A red **filter** will only let through red light:
It **absorbs** all the other colours:

g Which colour passes through a green filter?

h Which colours are absorbed by a green filter?

i Use this diagram to explain what you see when you look through a blue filter and a red filter together:

j Where have you seen filters used?

Seeing coloured objects

k The paper in this book looks white.
Write down which colours you think are being reflected from it.

l Use the diagram to explain what happens when white light shines on green paper:

m Explain what is happening when you look at this red ink.

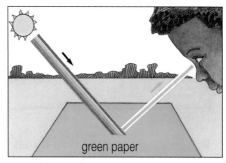

Green things reflect green light and absorb the other colours. We see the green light.

Designing for the stage

Imagine you are the stage-designer for a pop group.
You have to design the band's clothes as well as the stage colours. The manager tells you that the stage lights will flash red or green or blue.
The picture shows someone's first attempt:

- Look at this picture in red light, in green light, and in blue light. (Or look through filters.)

- Draw up a table to show what colours a white, a red, a green and a blue object look like in white, red, green and blue lights.

- Then re-design the set and the clothes so that the band can be seen better.

Safety first

Plan an investigation to see which is the safest colour for you to wear when riding a bicycle, or walking on a road.

- How will you make it a fair test?

- How will you find out which is the safest colour for both day-time and night-time?

- Show your plan to your teacher and, if you have time, do it.

- How else can you improve your safety on the road?

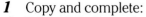

Things to do

1 Copy and complete:
a) White light is . . . . by a prism into a spectrum. The 7 colours are:
b) . . . . light has the longest wavelength.
c) The colour refracted the most is . . . .
d) A red filter lets . . . . light through, and . . . . all the other colours.
e) A blue T-shirt reflects . . . . light, and . . . . all the other colours.

2 What colour would a red book look:
a) in red light?   c) through a red filter?
b) in green light?   d) through a blue filter?

3 Which jobs may be dangerous or difficult if you are colour-blind?

4 Plan an investigation to see which colours are best for an easy-to-read disco poster.

26d

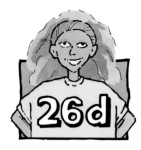

Musical sounds

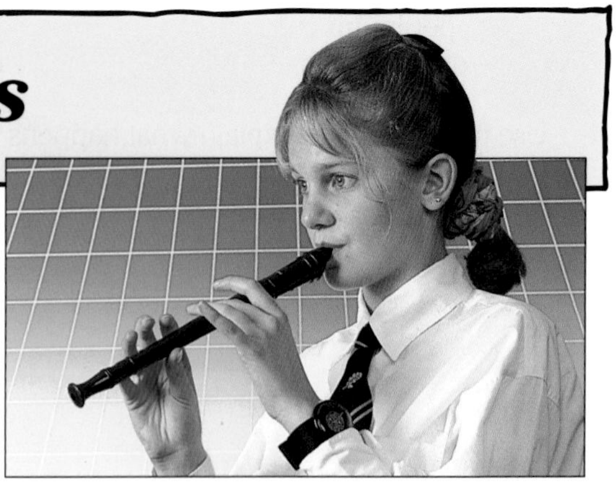

▶ Touch the front of your throat while you say 'aaah'.
Can you feel it ***vibrating*?**

a Explain, step by step, how someone else can hear this sound.

b What is vibrating in 1) a guitar**?**
2) a drum**?**
3) the recorder in the photo**?**

Waves on a spring

You can use a 'slinky' spring to 'model' a sound wave.
When you vibrate the end, a wave of energy travels down the spring:

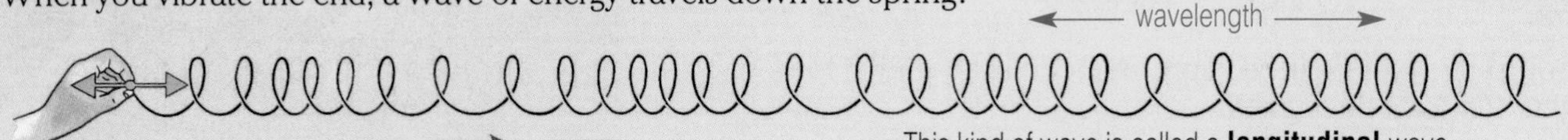

wavelength
energy
This kind of wave is called a **longitudinal** wave.

When you speak, the sound energy travels through the air. It is the **molecules** of air that vibrate:

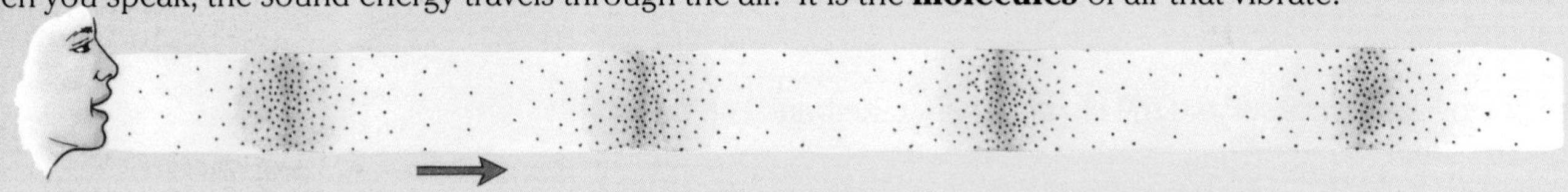

The energy is transferred from molecule to molecule. They vibrate like the coils of the spring.

c Why can't sound travel through a vacuum**?**

An oscilloscope

You can use a **c**athode **r**ay **o**scilloscope (**CRO**) to investigate sound waves.

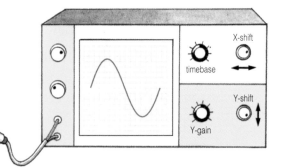

The sound energy enters the microphone. The energy is transferred to electrical energy, which goes to the oscilloscope. A graph of the wave is shown on the screen:

X-shift
timebase
Y-shift
Y-gain

What happens if you 1) turn the Y-shift knob**?**
2) turn the X-shift knob**?**
3) switch the time-base off and on**?**
4) change the Y-gain dial**?**

Loudness and amplitude

- Hum or whistle a quiet sound into the microphone.
- Then do the same sound but ***louder***.
  How does the wave change**?**
- Sketch the 2 waves.
- How does the **amplitude** of a wave depend on the loudness of the sound**?**

amplitude

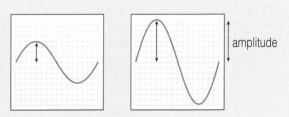

Which note is louder?

Pitch and frequency

- Hum or whistle a note with a low pitch, and then a high pitch. How does the wave change?

- Sketch the 2 waves.

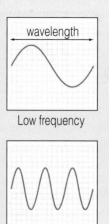

wavelength

Low frequency

High frequency

Which note is high-pitched?

- Waves with a shorter wavelength have a higher *frequency*. The molecules are vibrating more often. Frequency is measured in **hertz** (**Hz**). A note of 300 Hz means it is vibrating 300 times in each second.

- How does the pitch of your notes depend on the frequency?

- Blow a dog-whistle. What do you notice? What is ultrasound?

- Connect a signal-generator to a loudspeaker, to make sound waves of different frequencies. What is the highest note you can hear? Sketch its wave.

Musical instruments

- Make different sounds – aaah, ooo, eee – while you watch the screen.

- Play different musical instruments. Play the same note on each one, and sketch the waves.

- In what ways are the waves 1) the same? 2) different?

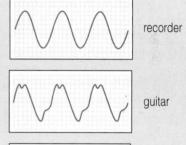

recorder

guitar

violin

---

1 Copy and complete:
a) A sound . . . . is caused by vibrations. It is a . . . . wave. The energy is transferred from molecule to . . . .
b) A loud sound has a large . . . .
c) A high-pitched sound has a high . . . .
d) Frequency is measured in . . . . (Hz).

2 Write down the names of 10 musical instruments that do not use electricity. For each one, say whether it is plucked, blown, bowed, hit or shaken.

3 Humming birds make a noise by beating their wings very quickly. Plan an investigation to find out the frequency at which their wings vibrate.

4 The diagrams below show 4 waves.
a) Which has the largest amplitude?
b) Which has the highest frequency?
c) Which was the quietest sound?
d) Which sound had the lowest pitch?
e) Which 2 have the same amplitude?
f) Which 2 have the same frequency?

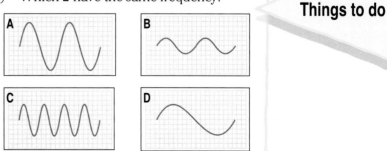

Things to do

129

26e

Hear, hear

▶ Why do some people wear a hearing aid?
Do you know anyone who wears one?
What do you think is inside a hearing aid?

Your ear can easily be damaged. This causes deafness.
You looked at this in *Spotlight Science for Scotland S1*.

a In what ways can your ear be damaged?
Write down as much as you can remember about this.

How loud?

If you stand too close to a loudspeaker in a disco, you could damage your hearing.
Does it matter *where* you stand? Plan an investigation to find out.

• What will you use to detect the sound?

• How will you keep a record of the different positions that you try?

• Predict what you think you will find.

• If you have time, try it.

Sound levels

The chart shows some data about loudness levels, which are measured in decibels (dB):

(The loudness levels are a rough guide, but actual values depend on the exact situation.)

b Continuous noise levels of 90 dB or more can damage your hearing.
Make a list of any of these situations in your life.

c The loudness shown for a rock concert depends on whether it is inside a hall or in the open-air.
Why do you think this is?

d The damage depends on the loudness level *and* the length of time you listen to it.
For how long is it safe to listen (without a break) to a personal stereo at 110 dB?

e Look at the list of exposure times.
There is a pattern. Describe the pattern you see.

f Professional rock musicians wear expensive ear-plugs. Why do you think they are each specially made to be close-fitting in the musician's ear?

Approx. loudness in decibels		Maximum safe exposure time
140	boom stereo in car, jet engine at 100 ft	–
130	rock concert indoors	–
120	rock concert outdoors, loud stereo in car	7½ mins
110	personal stereo full on; some cinemas	30 mins
100	personal stereo on 6/10 setting	2 hours
90	loud party, motorbike, train	8 hours
80	school canteen, traffic noise in car	
70		
60	conversation	
50		
40		
30	whispering	
20		
10		

Speed of sound

▶ Joanne sees a lightning flash on a hill which she knows is 1000 metres away. She hears the sound 3 seconds later.

g Which travels faster, sound or light?

h Use the formula:

$$\text{speed} = \frac{\text{distance travelled}}{\text{time taken}}$$

to calculate the speed of sound in air.

▶ Sound can travel through solids, liquids and gases.

i What can you say about the particles in a solid compared with the particles in a gas?

j Can you use this idea to explain why sound travels faster in a solid than in a gas?

k Does sound travel faster in water or in air?

Echoes

Sailors can use **echoes** to find the depth of the sea:

▶ Suppose this ship sent out a sound wave, and got back an echo after 1 second.

l How long did it take for the sound to get down to the bottom?

m How far does the sound travel in this time? (The speed of sound in water is 1500 metres per second.)

n How deep is the sea?

o If the fish are 250 m deep, what would be their echo time?

p The boat then moves into very deep water. Explain why it is harder to detect the echo.

Reflecting a sound

Plan an experiment to see if the angle of incidence is equal to the angle of reflection for a sound wave.

Things to do

1 Copy and complete:
a) Light travels . . . . than sound.
b) The formula for speed is:
c) Sound travels . . . . in iron than in water. It travels . . . . in water than in air.
d) When sound is reflected, you get an . . . . This is used in . . . . -sounding.
e) Ear damage depends on the . . . . level and the length of . . . . you listen to it.

2 Make a list of jobs you could not do if your hearing was damaged.

3 If you hear thunder 15 seconds after seeing lightning, how far away is the storm? (Speed of sound = 330 m/s)

4 Do you think background music in shops persuades people to buy more things? Plan an investigation to answer this.

5 School canteens are usually very noisy. How could you make yours quieter? Draw a plan of it and label all the improvements you would make if you were an architect.

Physics at Work

Road safety

In the photo, the coat and the road-sign contain thousands of tiny shiny beads that act like mirrors.

a Explain why the man's coat looks brighter than his face.

b What does this say?

c Why is it written like this?

d How should the word STOP be written on a sign on the front of a police car?

Use these 3 ray diagrams to explain, in your own words, and with examples, the meanings of:

e transparent,

f translucent,

g opaque.

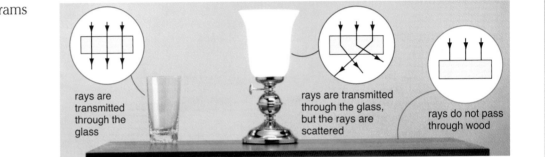

rays are transmitted through the glass

rays are transmitted through the glass, but the rays are scattered

rays do not pass through wood

Autocue

Politicians and newsreaders often use an autocue.
It lets them talk directly at the audience, so they don't have to look down at their notes, or memorise them.

h Use the diagram to explain why the speaker can see the words.

i Explain why the audience can't see the words.

j Look at the way the words are written on the projector. Why is this?

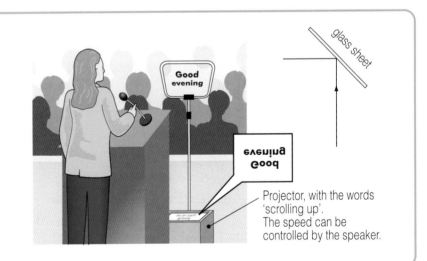

Good evening

glass sheet

Good evening

Projector, with the words 'scrolling up'.
The speed can be controlled by the speaker.

Red + Green + Blue

The picture shows 3 spotlights shining on a screen:

k What colour do you get where the red + green overlap?

A **TV screen** has tiny spots of red, green and blue on it.

l What is happening when you see yellow on the TV screen?

Curved mirrors

The photo shows a convex curved mirror (like the back of a spoon).

It is placed on a busy road opposite the exit of a house.

m What is the mirror for?

n Why is a convex mirror better than a plane mirror?

Astronauts

These astronauts can see each other, but they can't hear each other except on the radio.

What does this tell you about:
o light waves?
p sound waves?
q radio waves?

r How would this change if they stood together with their helmets touching?

Seeing double

If you look at the image of your face in a mirror, you can often see a faint second image of your face.

Use the diagram to explain:

s Why do you see a second image?

t Why is it faint?

glass

silvering

Whales can 'sing' messages to each other. They can hear each other a hundred miles away through the sea (but not through the air).
u Try to use particle theory (molecules) to explain why sound travels farther in water than in air.

Bats and **dolphins** use ultrasound to find food and 'see' in the dark.

v What is ultrasound?

w How do the bats and dolphins use it?

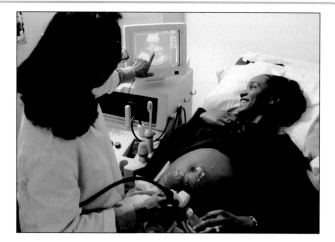

An ultrasonic **scanner** is used to look at a baby inside the mother's womb. It works like the echo-sounder on a ship.

x Explain how you think it works.

Geologists use **echo-sounding** to search for oil and gas.

y In the diagram, which microphone will receive the sound first?

z The speed of sound in rock is about 4000 m/s. If the sound arrives at the microphone after $\frac{1}{2}$ second, estimate the depth of the hard rock layer.

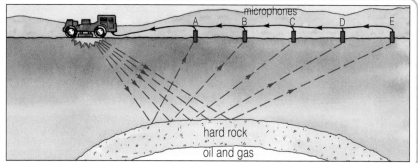

microphones

A   B   C   D   E

hard rock

oil and gas

Questions

1 Suppose you can choose from a variety of mirrors (plane and curved) and lenses (converging and diverging). Work out a design for each of these:

a) a torch
b) a periscope to see at a football match
c) a periscope to see behind you in a car
d) a solar cooker
e) a spy camera to take photos round corners
f) an over-head projector for a teacher.

Draw a labelled diagram of each design. On each diagram, draw coloured lines to show what happens to the rays of light.

2 Natalya is only 3 years old. She can speak but she can't read yet, so it is hard to use the usual eye-test with her: Design a test that could be used instead.

3 Some pupils were hypothesising about the effects of colour.

Anna said, "I think more people choose to eat green jelly than any other colour."
Jamie said, "I think that flies are more likely to land on yellow surfaces than white surfaces."

Choose one of these hypotheses, and plan an investigation to test it. Take care to make it a fair test.

4 The diagram shows the path of 2 rays of light from a fish to a fisherman:

a) Use the diagram to explain why the fisherman should not aim his spear directly where he sees the fish.
b) Why does water always appear shallower than it really is?

5 Kelly says, "There ought to be a law against playing music loudly." Do you agree with her?
Give your arguments for and against this idea.

6 The diagram shows a wave-form on an oscilloscope:

a) What is the time taken for 1 wave?
b) How many waves are there in 100 milliseconds?
c) How many waves will there be in 1 second?
   (1 second = 1000 milliseconds)
d) What is the frequency of the wave?
e) Would this be a high note or a low note?

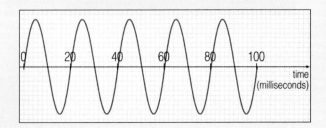

7 The time-keeper of a 100 m race stands at the finishing line. He starts his stop-watch when he hears the starter's pistol.

a) Will the time he measures be too long or too short?
b) By how much? (Speed of sound in air = 340 m/s)

Micro organisms

27

In the air around us and on everything we touch there are organisms that are so small that we cannot see them unless we look at them through a powerful microscope. These tiny organisms are called microorganisms.

In this topic you will find out how some microorganisms cause disease and how our bodies can fight them to help us to recover.

You will also learn about enzymes and how important they are both in our bodies and in modern biotechnology.

Different kinds of microorganisms

Microorganism is the name we give to an organism that is so small that it can only be seen through a microscope.

Only a few hundred years ago nobody had ever heard of a microorganism. People didn't have a clue why foods rotted or how diseases were passed from one person to another.

Eventually, thanks to the work of scientists like the great Frenchman Louis Pasteur, it was shown that microorganisms are responsible for making food rot and for many diseases.

a What process gets its name from **Louis Pasteur?**

There are 3 different types of microorganisms: bacteria, viruses and fungi.

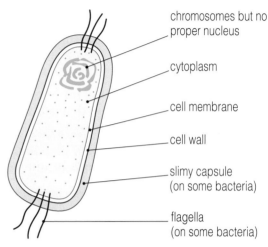

chromosomes but no proper nucleus

cytoplasm

cell membrane

cell wall

slimy capsule (on some bacteria)

flagella (on some bacteria)

A bacterium

Bacteria

Bacteria are single cells. They are so small that if 100 were lined up end-to-end they would only stretch about 1 mm.

b In what ways does a bacterium resemble an animal cell or a plant cell? In what ways is it different?

A bacterium doesn't have a proper nucleus. The thread-shaped chromosomes are simply coiled up in the middle of the cell. Although the bacterium has a cell wall, this is not made of cellulose as it would be in a plant cell.

Some bacteria have whip-like flagella that help them to move around. Others are protected from drying out by a slimy capsule.

Bacteria come in different groups according to their shape.

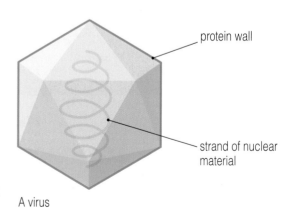

sphere (coccus)

spiral (spirillum)

rod (bacillus)

Different forms of bacteria

Viruses

Viruses are even smaller than bacteria. A typical bacterium is about one hundred times bigger than a typical virus.

c How many viruses lined up end-to-end would be needed to stretch 1 mm?

Viruses come in a variety of shapes and sizes.

Viruses are the simplest of all organisms. A virus has neither a nucleus nor cytoplasm so we cannot call it a cell. It is simply a strand of nuclear material surrounded by a protein wall.

Viruses can only reproduce inside the cells of living organisms. The cells may belong to an animal, a plant or even a bacterium. This is why viruses can be so harmful to other organisms.

protein wall

strand of nuclear material

A virus

Fungi

Fungi have no chlorophyll and so they cannot make food by photosynthesis. Instead, they feed on ready-made organic food. Some fungi are **saprophytes** and feed on dead and decaying material, while others are **parasites** and feed on living organisms.

A fungus is not composed of cells but of **hyphae**.
These hyphae have a lining of cytoplasm containing many small nuclei. At the end of each hypha special chemicals called **enzymes** are secreted.
They break down the food so it can be absorbed into the cytoplasm through the cell wall.

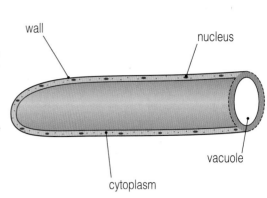

Structure of a hypha

Mucor is the name given to a type of mould that grow on the surface of decaying fruit, bread and other organic material. Moulds like this are simply a mass of hyphae that spread out as the mould grows.

The **yeasts** are an unusual group of fungi. Most are composed of separate cells rather than hyphae. Yeast has been used for centuries for making wine and other alcoholic drinks, and for baking bread.

Mouldy bread

Colonies

It is much easier to see a large group of microorganisms than a single one. Fortunately, they grow very quickly so if we give them the right conditions – moisture, warmth and food – a few microorganisms will grow in to a colony of millions almost overnight.

Agar gel is a nutritious jelly. It is an ideal medium for growing bacteria. Bacteria colonies vary in size, shape and colour according to what type they are. These features can be used to identify bacteria.

d Why is it important to
   i) sterilise the plate before adding the agar gel?
   ii) cover the plate and seal it from the air?
   iii) dispose of the used plate safely?

Viruses cannot be grown easily in the school laboratory. They don't grow on agar gel but need living cells in order to multiply.

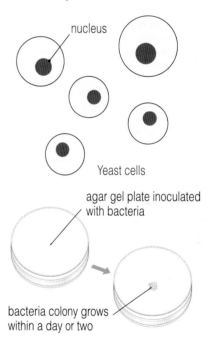

Yeast cells

agar gel plate inoculated with bacteria

bacteria colony grows within a day or two

---

1 Name 3 types of microorganisms.

2 These bacteria all cause diseases:

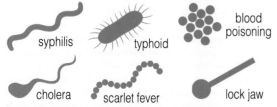

Look at the shape of each bacterium. To which group does the bacterium that causes each disease belong, sphere, rod or spiral?

3 Yeast cells will grow and reproduce in glucose solution. Under suitable conditions the number of yeast cells will double in number every hour.
a) Starting with one yeast cell, calculate how many yeast cells there would be after one hour, two hours, etc. for a whole day. Write your results in a table.
b) Plot a graph of the number of yeast cells against time for a day. What shape is your graph?
c) Would the number of yeast cells keep on going up? Explain your answer.

Things to do

Microorganisms and disease

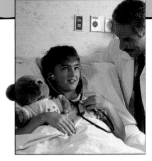

Do you know why people get ill?

▶ Make a list of some of the things that you think make people ill.

Your skin acts as a barrier to microorganisms.

a Can you remember the main types of microorganisms?

Bacteria and viruses are a common cause of disease.

b Make a list of some diseases caused by these microorganisms.

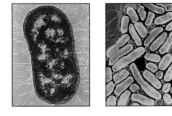

The **symptoms** of a disease are the body's response to waste chemicals made by the microorganisms.

c Write down some symptoms that you know of.

Points of entry

Look at these ways in which diseases can be spread:

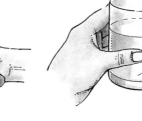

| air | food | touch | water | animals |

d For each method shown in the picture, write down:
  i) A disease that can be spread in this way (your teacher can give you a Help Sheet).
  ii) How its spread can be prevented.

e Can you think of any other ways in which diseases can be spread?

▶ Use your Help Sheet of diseases to find out the answers to the following questions.

f What type of microorganism causes   i) tuberculosis?   ii) measles?   iii) athlete's foot?

g What are the symptoms of   i) polio?   ii) mumps?   iii) the common cold?

h How are   i) malaria   ii) rubella, and   iii) athlete's foot spread?

Seldomill Health Authority
Memo to: Analysts   **From:** Mike Robe

The children at Sick Lee High School have been going down with severe stomach upsets. I think that the disease may be linked to places where they eat their lunch. These are the school canteen, the Greasy Cod Chip Shop, Sid's Snack Bar and Betty's Bakery.
Please plan an investigation to find out the source of infection. Write me a report about your plan, the tests you intend to use, and how you will show your results.

Please hurry!

Antibiotics: useful drugs

Your doctor might give you an **antibiotic** to help you fight a disease.
The first antibiotic was discovered by Alexander Fleming.

Bother, some mould has got on to this agar plate. The bacteria aren't growing well.

I wonder if the mould is making a chemical that kills off bacteria.

Just like Fleming!

- Using sterile forceps, place a sterile paper disc into each of:

  A – disinfectant   **B** – alcohol   **C** – crystal violet
  D – washing-up liquid

- Leave to soak for 5 minutes.

- You will be given an agar plate which has harmless bacteria growing on it.

- Divide the underneath of an agar plate into 6 sections and label them **A** to **F**.

- Remove the discs with sterile forceps and shake off any excess liquid.

- Place each disc on the correct part of the agar plate.

- Your teacher will give you a **penicillin** and a **streptomycin** disc for sectors **E** and **F**.

- Sellotape the lid to the base so it cannot come off.

- Incubate your plate for 48 hours at 25°C. Then examine the growth of bacteria.

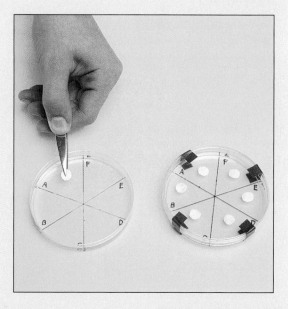

i   Which chemical had most effect upon the growth of the bacteria?

j   How were you able to measure this effect?

k   How could you use this test to find out the best concentration of an antibiotic to use?

---

1   Copy and complete:
Bacteria and . . . . are the main microorganisms that cause disease. The . . . . of a disease are caused by chemicals made by the microorganisms. A drug that fights the disease inside your body is called an . . . .
Alexander . . . . discovered one of the first antibiotics.

2   Name 4 ways in which diseases can be spread. For each way say how you think the disease can be prevented.

3   Drugs that kill microorganisms inside the body are called **antibiotics**.
Find out what **antiseptics** and **disinfectants** are and how they help to fight disease.

4   How do you think the following can help to spread disease:
a) flies?
b) hypodermic needles?
c) kitchen clothes?

Things to do

Self-defence

How is it that our bodies are able to fight off disease? If you catch a disease like measles, you don't get it again – you become **immune**.

Why do you think this happens? Write down your ideas.

Fighting off the enemy

All germs (that's bacteria and viruses) have chemicals on their surfaces. These chemicals are called **antigens**.
When you catch a disease like measles, the white blood cells in your body make chemicals called **antibodies**.
These antibodies attach themselves to the antigens on the surface of the germs.
They cause the germs to clump together and make them harmless.
Now another type of white blood cell, let's call them 'killer cells', are able to 'eat' the 'stuck-together' germs.

After any disease, the antibodies stay in your blood, making you immune.

a So how can you become immune to some diseases and not others?

Each germ has antigens of a particular shape. So you produce antibodies that match the shape of each antigen. This is why you have to catch the disease before you become immune to it.

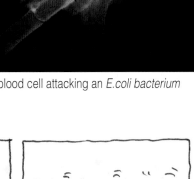

A white blood cell attacking an *E.coli bacterium*

1. Bacteria enter your body through a cut in your skin.

2. Your body makes antibodies to fight the invaders.

3. The bacteria are destroyed by the antibodies.

4. Antibodies stand by ready to fight off any future attack. The body is **immune**.

▶ Study the cartoons and use the information to write a brief explanation of what happens when harmful bacteria invade your body.

You can also become immune to a disease by **vaccination**. A vaccine is a weak form of the disease microbe.

b Explain how you think vaccination works.
c Your body can make millions of *different* antibodies. Why do you think this is?

d Find out how **antiseptics** kill germs outside your body.

Disinfectants are strong chemicals that kill germs on floors and work surfaces.

e Why are **disinfectants** not used to kill germs on or in our bodies?

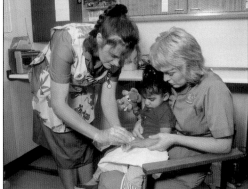

A toddler being vaccinated

Mr Clean

Bob is the caretaker at the high school.
He's got a problem.
The label has come off his big bottle of disinfectant.
So he doesn't know how much to add to water before use.
If he adds too little, it won't kill the germs.
If he adds too much, it'll be expensive.
Help Bob out by finding the **smallest** amount of disinfectant that will kill the germs.

(Hint: You could use agar plates and paper discs with different concentrations of disinfectant on them.)

Your teacher will give you an agar plate with harmless bacteria growing on it.

How much disinfectant will you add?

How will you make it a **fair test**?

How long will you leave it to work?

How will you record your results?

Ask your teacher to check your plan, then try it out.

Things to do

1 Copy and complete:
If you catch a disease and you don't get it again, you are . . . . to it.
Your body makes chemicals called . . . .
They stick the germs together and make them . . . .
The . . . . stay in your blood to give you immunity to the disease. A . . . . is a weak form of the disease microorganism. It can be . . . . into your body or taken by mouth. It gives you . . . . to a disease.

2 Find out whether the following are true or false.
a) Tetanus is caused by germs getting into an open wound.
b) A pregnant woman cannot pass on rubella to her unborn child.
c) Smallpox vaccine is no longer given because the disease has been wiped out.
d) There is a low risk of whooping cough vaccine causing brain damage to some babies.

3 Why is it important that the following places are free from germs?
a) Swimming pools.
b) School kitchens.
c) Doctor's surgeries.

4 Try to find out what diseases people can be vaccinated against.
Which vaccines have you been given?

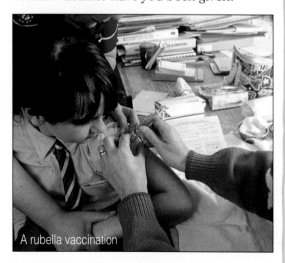

A rubella vaccination

Enzymes

27d

Imagine trying to carry out lots of different chemical reactions in the same test-tube at the same time.

This is exactly what is going on, all of the time, in each of the cells of our bodies. How is it that different reactions can go on at the same time without interfering with each other? The answer is **enzymes**.

Enzymes work in the same way as **catalysts**.

a How do catalysts help in the production of oxygen from hydrogen peroxide?

Enzymes also control the rates of chemical reactions but not just any chemical reaction. Each enzyme controls a particular reaction.

A key to fit the lock

Enzyme molecules are long and twisted so they have an irregular shape. Each enzyme has a different shape.

An enzyme only works on reactant molecules that have a shape that fits them. The enzyme is a bit like a lock and the reactant molecule is the key. The lock only works if the key fits exactly.

It is for this reason that lots of enzyme can control different reactions in a cell without getting in each other's way.

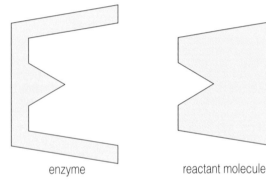

enzyme   reactant molecule

Enzymes and temperature

b What effect does heat have on the rate of a chemical reaction?

We often heat chemical reactions in the laboratory to make them go faster. The activity of an enzyme also increases with temperature up to a point called the **optimum temperature** for the enzyme. However, beyond the optimum temperature the activity of the enzyme drops very quickly to zero.

c Why do you think this happens?

The increasing temperature eventually causes the enzyme to change its shape. The reactant molecules no longer fit. The enzyme has been denatured (but not killed – although enzymes work in a clever way, they are not living things).

d What do you think is the optimum temperature for the enzymes in our bodies?

Enzymes are used widely in the manufacture of processed foods, and in brewing.

The optimum temperature of some of these enzymes is over 80°C and they work over a variety of acidic and alkaline conditions.

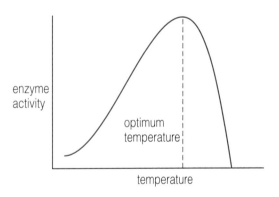

Enzymes and pH

Each enzyme works best at a particular pH value. If the pH moves above or below this **optimum pH** value the activity of the enzyme decreases. Changes in pH alter the shape of an enzyme, making it more difficult for the reactant molecules to fit.

Enzymes are needed to digest food. The optimum pH value of each of the digestive enzymes in the gut depends on where it is found. Some enzymes work in the stomach where it is acidic while others work in the small intestine where it is alkaline.

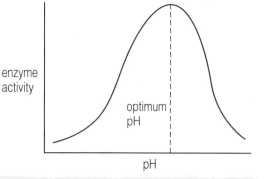

Pepsin – acidic or alkaline?

Pepsin is an enzyme that breaks down protein molecules into smaller molecules called peptides. In this investigation the source of protein is egg white.

- Your teacher will give you a cloudy suspension of egg white.
- Pour 5 cm³ of suspension into each of four test-tubes. Label your test-tubes A, B, C and D.
- To tube A, add 1 cm³ of 1% pepsin solution.
- To tube B, add 1 cm³ of 1% pepsin solution and 3 drops of dilute hydrochloric acid.
- To tube C, add 1 cm³ of distilled water.
- To tube D, add 1 cm³ of 1% pepsin solution and 3 drops of dilute sodium carbonate.
- Place the tubes in a beaker of warm water at 35–40°C and examine them at regular intervals. As the egg white is digested, the solution will become less cloudy and will eventually clear.

e What happens to the egg white in each tube?

f Under what conditions does pepsin work best?

g Where in the alimentary canal is pepsin found?

h What was the point of setting up tube C?

---

1 Copy and complete:
a) An enzyme controls the . . . . of a chemical reaction.
b) An enzyme controls a particular reaction. The enzyme and the reactant molecule fit together like a . . . . and . . . .
c) If an enzyme-controlled reaction is heated to a high temperature the reaction may stop because the enzyme becomes . . . .

2 The rate of most chemical reactions increases as the temperature increases. Explain why this is only true up to a point for reactions involving enzymes.

3 Pepsin is only one of a group of enzymes found in the gut.
Find out the names of some other digestive enzymes. In which part of the gut are they found? Do they work in acidic or alkaline conditions?

4 Alcalase is an enzyme used in the manufacture of soya bean products.

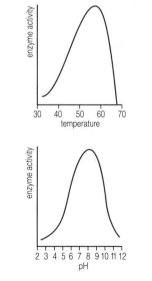

Use the graph to find out the optimum conditions for alcalase.

Things to do

Biotechnology

Biotechnology is concerned with the way in which we use microorganisms to produce substances that are useful to people. Much of this technology has been developed over the last half century but some has been with us a lot longer than that.

The ploughman's lunch

Thousands of years ago people were using bacteria to turn milk into yoghurt and cheese. They were also using yeast to make bread, and fermenting carbohydrates to make alcoholic drinks like wine and beer.

a Mead is another alcoholic drink that has been made for thousands of years. What is it made from**?**

If wine is left open to the air it turns to vinegar.
This can be used to preserve foods like onions.

All of the foods in our ploughman's meal are products of biotechnology.

The products of biotechnology were eaten and drunk long before the word 'biotechnology' was invented.

In a ferment

Yeast is a single-celled fungus. In the absence of air (anaerobic) yeast cells convert sugars into ethanol and carbon dioxide.

$$\text{sugars} \xrightarrow{\text{yeast}} \text{ethanol} + \text{carbon dioxide}$$

This process is called **anaerobic fermentation**.

In bread-making, yeast is added to the mixture of flour and water.
Enzymes in the flour turn some of the starch into sugar.
During proving, the sugar is rapidly fermented by yeast, producing bubbles of carbon dioxide in the dough.
This makes the dough rise when it is baked.

b Why is the dough put somewhere warm to prove**?**

Ethanol is also produced in the dough during bread-making but you don't need to worry about getting drunk when you next eat your sandwiches. The ethanol is destroyed as the bread bakes by the high temperature inside the oven.

In brewing the ethanol plays a more important part than the carbon dioxide gas.

Do any of your relatives brew their own wine? If they do you might have seen some big glass containers of sugary solution fermenting in their kitchen.

Wine is made by fermenting fruit juices

A new answer to an old problem

Insulin is an important chemical in our bodies. It is made in the pancreas and allows the cells of the body to absorb the sugar that builds up in the blood after we have eaten. Some people, about two in one hundred, cannot make enough insulin to control their blood sugar level – they suffer from a disease called **diabetes**.

c Do you have a friend or relative who is diabetic? What special care do they take with their diet?

In the past, the only source of insulin was extracts from the pancreases of cows and pigs.
This worked but there were problems with it.

- Insulin from cows and pigs was not the same as human insulin. Some people became allergic to it.
- There was always the danger of transmitting a disease from an animal to a human.
- As the number of diabetics increased it was difficult to keep up with demand.

Scientists solved the problem by using genetic engineering to modify bacteria so that they produced an exact replica of human insulin.

Some diabetics must inject themselves with insulin.

Some microorganisms are good to eat

Eating microorganisms is not a new idea. People have been eating foods that contain microorganisms, like cheese and fungi, for many hundreds of years.

In Britain **brewer's yeasts** have been used to make foods for many years. Excess yeasts are sold as cattle food or processed to make food for humans like Marmite.

Have you ever eaten any foods containing Quorn?
Quorn is a myco-protein made by growing large quantities of the mould *Fusarium*. The myco-protein contains about 45% protein and is grown in such a way as to give it a texture similar to some types of meat.

There is a wide range of foods containing Quorn.

1
a) Write a word equation to show what happens during anaerobic fermentation.
b) Which product of anaerobic fermentation is most useful in:
   i) beer-making?
   ii) bread-making?
c) In some countries ethanol, made from the fermentation of sugar, is used as a fuel for motor cars.
   Think of some advantages of using ethanol in place of petrol.

2 Biological washing powders contain enzymes that allow clothes to be washed clean at lower temperatures than would otherwise be possible.
a) How do you think adding enzymes to washing powders can make them more efficient?

b) List some of the advantages of washing clothes at lower temperatures.
c) Can you think of any disadvantages of putting enzymes in washing powder? Think about what happens to the waste water.

3 Quorn is often used as a substitute for meat. You can buy ready-prepared meals containing Quorn from large supermarkets.
a) Make a list of the range of ready-prepared meals containing Quorn in your local supermarket.
b) Plan a meal using Quorn. Try to be original and don't just copy what is sold in the shops. Show your plan to your parents – perhaps they will help you to prepare the meal.

Things to do

Questions

1
a) Name 3 groups of microorganisms that can cause infectious disease.
b) Give 3 ways in which these microorganisms can be spread from one person to another.
c) The early stage of a disease is called the incubation period. What happens to the disease microorganism inside the body during the incubation period?
d) Disease microorganisms can damage tissues and release harmful chemicals called toxins that cause the symptoms of a disease. Give some examples of common disease symptoms.
e) Look at the graph:
   i) What symptom of the disease is shown on the graph?
   ii) How long was the incubation period?
   iii) What caused the fever and how long did it last?

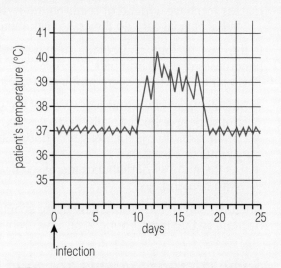

2
In Scotland, in 1997, a new strain of *E.coli* caused an outbreak of food poisoning that affected 500 people and killed 20. Read the newspaper report opposite:
a) How do you think the disease was spread?
b) Why did existing antibiotics prove useless?
c) Find out about other diseases which are increasing due to increased resistance to antibiotics.

Death toll rises in food bug outbreak

Five people have died of food poisoning in Britain's worst case of *E-coli bacteria* contamination.

A hospital has been closed to all GP-arranged admissions except suspected cases of the *E.coli 0157* food poisoning outbreak.

The butcher's shop thought to be the source of the outbreak announced yesterday that is was temporarily closing.

Seven members of staff linked to the food poisoning outbreak in Scotland are infected.

Thirty-two adults and a child were being treated yesterday in the hospital, where the Lanarkshire Infectious Disease Unit is based. The number giving cause for concern rose from ten to 15 over the weekend, and the number showing symptoms rose from 189 to 209.

3
Look at the picture. It shows some of the antibodies that Martin has in his blood.
a) Does Martin's blood contain antibodies to fight polio?
b) Is he immune to polio?
c) Can he catch polio?
d) Does Martin have the antibodies in his blood to fight measles?
e) Is he immune to measles?

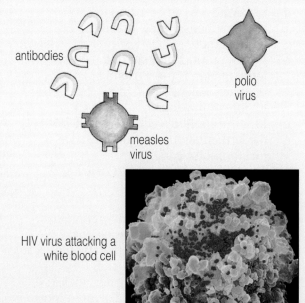

HIV virus attacking a white blood cell

4
AIDS is caused by the HIV virus, which attacks the body's immune system. The virus attacks the white blood cells that protect us.
HIV is only transmitted if the blood or semen (the fluid that contains sperms) of an infected person enters the blood stream of another person.
a) How could HIV be detected in a person?
b) How might HIV be transmitted by:
   i) the transfusion of infected blood?
   ii) drug addicts sharing needles?
   iii) sexual activity with many partners?
c) In each case in (b), suggest how the spread of HIV can be prevented.

Using forces

28

Your life is full of forces.
Everything that you do needs a force – a push or a pull.

You use forces to move around, and to transfer energy.

In this topic, we'll look at forces as they move, as they turn, and as they exert a pressure.

Just a moment

28a

▶ The diagram shows 2 spanners:
Which spanner would you use to turn a very tight nut?
How can you make it even easier to turn the nut?

▶ Which is the best place to push on a door to open it –
at the hinge or at the door edge?

▶ Some water-taps are hard for old people or invalids to
turn. Design a better tap for an old person.

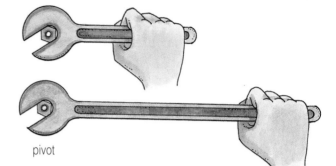

pivot

Hold a ruler at the very end, and put an object on it
(for example, a rubber):

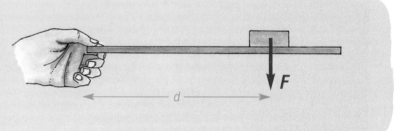

• Put the object at different positions on the ruler.
What do you notice?

• Try a heavier object, at different distances.

d

F

The turning effect depends on 2 things:
• the size of the force,
• the distance of the force from the pivot.

The turning effect of a force is called its **moment**.
The moment is calculated by:

Moment of the force =	**force** (in newtons)	×	**distance from pivot** (in metres)

Moments are measured in units called **newton-metre** (**Nm**).

Example 1

A car-driver is tightening a nut.

She exerts a 10 N force, 20 cm
from the nut:

← 20 cm →

10 N

How big is the turning effect?

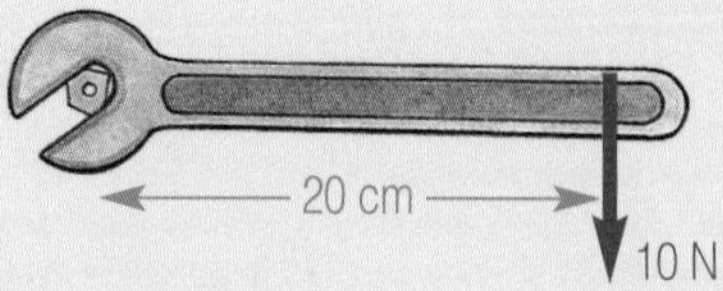

Answer

Distance from pivot = 20 cm = 0.2 m

Moment = force × distance from pivot

= 10 N × 0.2 m

= 2 Nm

---

a If the driver applies a force of 100 N,
40 cm from the pivot, what is the moment?

b A boy pushes a door with a force of 10 N,
60 cm from the hinge. What is the moment?

Moments in balance

Here is a see-saw:

The big girl has a moment which is turning in a clockwise direction.

c Which way is the small boy's moment turning?

d Why do you think that the small boy can balance the big girl?

When the see-saw is balanced, and not moving, it is 'in equilibrium'.

Then: | the **anti-clockwise moments** = the **clockwise moments** |

This is called **the principle of moments** (or **the law of levers**).

Testing the principle of moments

Your teacher can give you a Help Sheet for this.

- You can use a ruler as a see-saw, and add weights:

- Work out the clockwise and anti-clockwise moments. What do you find?

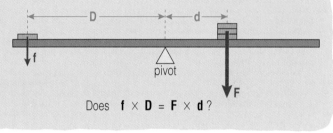

Does $f \times D = F \times d$?

Example 2

A pole-vaulter is holding the pole:

His left hand acts as a pivot.
You can assume that the weight of the pole (50 N) acts at the centre of the pole, 1 m from the pivot.
How hard must his right hand push down?

Answer

When balanced ('in equilibrium'):

anti-clockwise moments = clockwise moments

$$F \times 0.5 = 50 \times 1$$

$$F = \frac{50}{0.5} = \underline{100 \text{ newtons}}$$

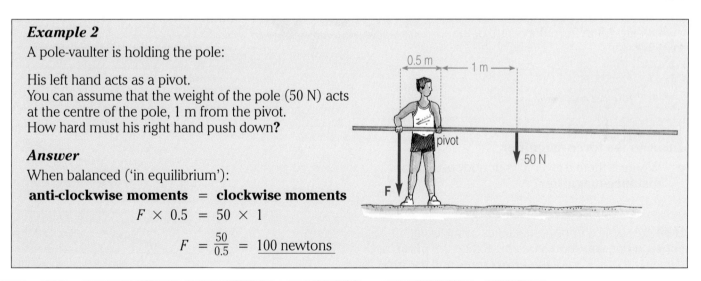

---

1 Copy and complete:
a) The turning effect (or . . . .) of a force is equal to the force multiplied by the . . . . from the . . . . Its unit is . . . .
b) The principle of moments states that, when an object is balanced and not moving, the anti-clockwise . . . . are . . . . to the . . . . moments.

2 Explain why it is difficult to steer a bike by gripping the centre of the handle-bars.

3 The diagrams show metre rules balanced at their centres.
What is the weight of a) *X*? and b) *Y*?

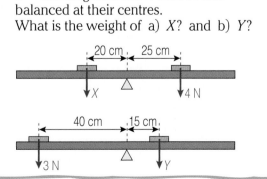

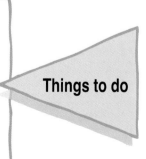

Things to do

28b Levers

In the last lesson you started to look at levers.
A lever is a simple **machine**. It helps us to
do work more easily.
Here is a lever being used to lift a big **load**:

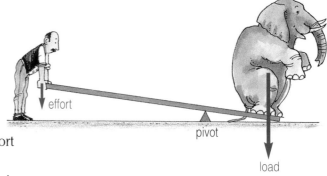

The lever can turn about a pivot (or 'fulcrum').
The man is applying an **effort** force.

a Where would you move the pivot to make the effort
even smaller?

b Which moves through a bigger distance – the man's
hands or the elephant?

Example

A wheelbarrow with its load weighs
300 newtons.

The weight acts at a distance of 0.5 m
from the centre of the wheel (the pivot).

What force is needed to lift the handles,
which are 1.5 m from the centre of the
wheel?

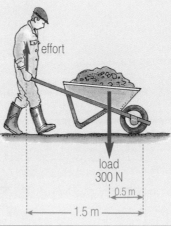

Answer

Use the principle of moments (p. 149).

When balanced ('in equilibrium'):

$$\left(\begin{array}{l} \text{clockwise} \\ \text{moment} \end{array} = \begin{array}{l} \text{anti-clockwise} \\ \text{moment} \end{array} \right)$$

$$\text{effort} \times 1.5 = 300 \times 0.5$$

$$\text{effort} = \underline{100 \text{ newtons}}$$

• Design a wheelbarrow that
would need even less effort.

This lever is a **force-magnifier**.

c Where is there a lever in your body used as a
distance-magnifier?

Here are some common machines using levers.
For each one you should be able to find the **pivot**, and
decide the positions of the **effort** force and the **load** force.
Your teacher will give you
a Help Sheet for this.

A balancing act

The gymnast is balanced on a beam:

Each part of her body is pulled down by gravity.

All the clockwise moments of the left-hand parts of her body are **balanced** by the anti-clockwise moments of the right-hand parts.

It's just as though all her weight is one force acting at one point **G**. G is called the **centre of gravity**.

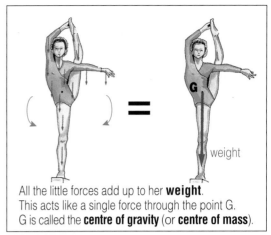

All the little forces add up to her **weight**. This acts like a single force through the point G. G is called the **centre of gravity** (or **centre of mass**).

d What would happen if her centre of gravity was not directly over her foot**?**

e Where is the centre of gravity of a metre rule**?**

Stability

If something is **stable**, it does not topple over. Use a box or match-box to investigate what makes an object stable.

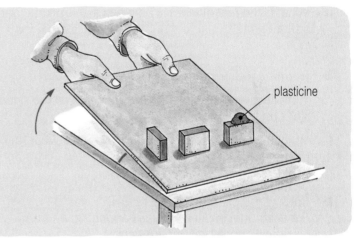

plasticine

• You can use plasticine to raise or lower the centre of gravity.

• To make the box more stable, should it have
  i) a high or a low centre of gravity**?**
  ii) a narrow or a wide base**?**

f Which is more stable: a racing-car or a double-decker bus**?**

g How are these 3 objects made stable**?**

Things to do

1 Copy and complete:
a) A lever can be a . . . .-magnifier or a . . . .-magnifier.
b) The centre of . . . . (centre of mass) is the point through which the whole . . . . of the object seems to act.
c) A stable object should have a . . . . centre of . . . ., and a . . . . base.

2 Which is more stable: a milk-bottle
a) full? or b) $\frac{1}{4}$-full of milk?
Draw diagrams of the bottles on a slope to explain your answer.

3 The diagram shows a tall crane with a counter-weight to balance the load.
a) Calculate the size of the counter-weight.
b) What can you say about the position of the centre of gravity?

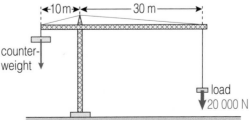

◀10 m▶◀———— 30 m ————▶

counter-weight ▼

load ▼20 000 N

28c *Under pressure*

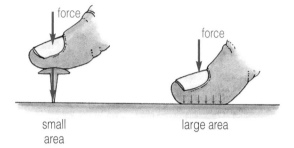
force   force

small area   large area

▶ You can push a drawing-pin into the table:

But you can't push your thumb into the table, even though you use a bigger force.

Why do you think this is?

▶ The pin-point has a small area. All the force is concentrated in that area, to give a high **pressure**.

With your thumb, the same force is spread out over a larger area. The pressure is smaller.

a What is the real difference between a sharp knife and a blunt knife?

▶ Here is another example:

Why does the boy sink into the snow, while the skier stays on top?

What are snow-shoes? Why do eskimoes wear them?

▶ Look at the pictures shown below.
For each one, explain what is happening, and why.
Use these words in your answers:

high/low **pressure**   **force**   small/large **area**

1 This bag is always hurting me.

2 No problem, but my heels keep getting stuck.

3 Which is best for a muddy garden?

4 This chair is always leaving marks on the carpet.

Can you solve this problem for me?

To calculate the pressure you need to know 2 things:
• the force exerted (in newtons)
• the area it is spread over (in cm² or m²).

In fact:

$$\textbf{Pressure} = \frac{\textbf{force} \text{ (in newtons)}}{\textbf{area} \text{ (in cm}^2 \text{ or m}^2)}$$

If the area is in cm², then the unit of pressure is newtons per square centimetre (**N/cm²**).

If the area is in m², then the unit of pressure is newtons per square metre (**N/m²**).
This unit is also called a **pascal** (**Pa**). 1 Pa = 1 N/m².

b Use the same method to calculate the pressure when a woman weighing 500 N stands on a stiletto heel of area 1 cm².

c Now compare these two pressures.
Which exerts the bigger pressure – the elephant or the shoe?
Which exerts the bigger force?

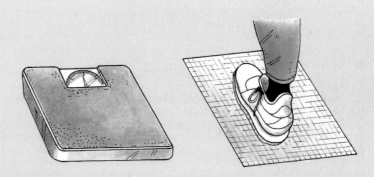

500 N

Shoe pressure

Plan a way to work out the pressure that you exert on the ground.

- Which 2 things do you have to measure?

- How can you do this?

- If you have time, do the investigation.

- Who makes the biggest and least pressures in your class?

---

1 Copy and complete:
a) The formula for pressure is:
b) Its units are . . . . per square centimetre (N/cm²) or . . . . per square metre (N/m², also called . . . .).

2 Explain the following:
a) It hurts to hold a heavy parcel by the string.
b) It is more comfortable to sit on a bed than on a fence.
c) Heavy lorries may have 8 rear wheels.

3 Design a beach-chair suitable for use on soft sand. Sketch your design.

4 What is the pressure when a force of 12 N pushes on an area of 2 square metres?

5 A man weighs 800 N. The total area of his 2 shoes is 400 cm².
a) What is the pressure on the ground?
b) He puts on some snow-shoes of total area 1600 cm². What is the pressure now?

6 This box weighs 100 N.
a) Calculate the area of each face.
b) Calculate the pressures when i) the red,   ii) the yellow, and iii) the blue faces are on the ground.

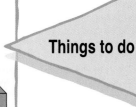

5 cm   10 cm   2 cm

Things to do

153

Pressure all around

Pressure in liquids

▶ Why do you think deep-sea divers have to wear special clothes?
Why do submarines have to be strong?

Yes – it is because of the **pressure** on them.

▶ Water is surprisingly heavy. A tank of goldfish
probably weighs more than you do!

The weight of water presses down and exerts a pressure.
As a fish swims deeper, the pressure on it increases
more and more.

This tank has 3 holes in the side:

You can see that the water is spurting out under pressure.

Which jet of water is spurting out farthest?

Where is the pressure greatest – at A, B, or C?

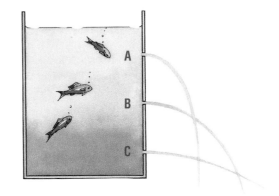

▶ Here is a side-view of a lake made by a dam:

The length of each arrow shows the size of the pressure.

a Where is the pressure least?

b Where is the pressure greatest?

c Why does the dam need to be thicker at
the bottom than at the top?

d Which forces are holding up the boat?
These forces are called the **upthrust**.

e The weight of the boat is 1000 N.
Where does this force act?

f The upthrust and the weight of the boat
are **balanced** forces. What does this mean?

g How big is the upthrust in this case?

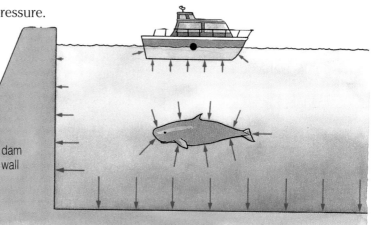

dam
wall

▶ The pressure of a liquid can be used to
work **hydraulic** machines:

What happens if you push in piston A?

Where is this used on a car?

syringe   water

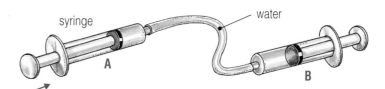

A   B

Pressure of air

Just as fish live at the bottom of a sea of water, we are living at the bottom of a 'sea' of air.
This air is called the **atmosphere**.

It exerts a pressure on us (just as the sea squeezes a fish).
This is called **atmospheric pressure**.

▶ If you blow up a balloon, you blow millions of tiny air **molecules** into it:

These molecules bounce around inside the balloon. Whenever a molecule hits the balloon, it gives the rubber a tiny push. Millions of these tiny pushes add up, to make the air pressure.

You are being punched on the nose billions of times each second by these tiny air molecules!

Can it be crushed?

Your teacher will show you an experiment with a metal can:

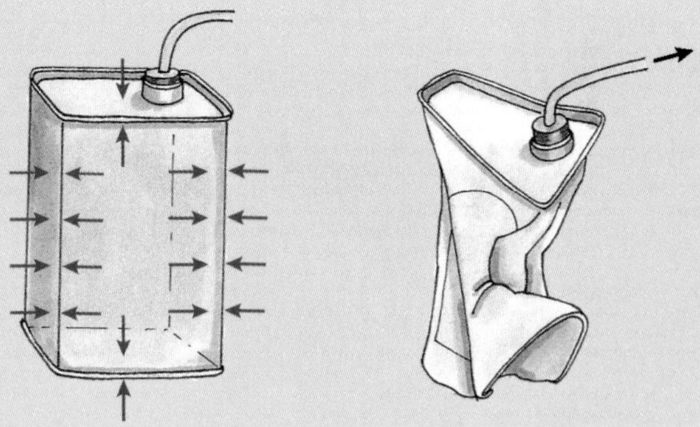

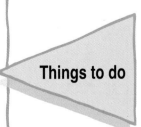

to vacuum pump

- At the start, the can has air inside and outside.
  The air molecules are bouncing on the inside and the outside.

- If a pump is used to take the air out of the can, what happens?

- Can you explain this? Try to use these words:
  molecules   air pressure

Sucking a straw

When you 'suck' on a straw, you use your lungs to lower the pressure inside the straw.

Explain why the liquid moves up, using these words:
molecules   air pressure

---

1 Copy and complete:
a) The pressure in a liquid is . . . . at the bottom than at the top.
b) A boat floats because the water pressure makes an . . . . force on it.
c) Air pressure is caused by billions of tiny . . . . bouncing around.

2 What happens to the air pressure as you go up a mountain? Why is this?

3 Explain why:
a) You can fill a bucket from a downstairs tap faster than from an upstairs tap.
b) Aeroplanes are often 'pressurised'.
c) Astronauts wear space-suits.

4 Alex says, "A vacuum cleaner works rather like a drinking straw."
Explain what you think he means, using the words: molecule, pressure.

Things to do

Physics at Work

Athletics

Here is a distance–time graph for a sprinter:

a What is happening in part C?

b How long is the race in
(i) distance? (ii) time?

c What was her average speed?

d Why is the graph curved at A?

e Can you sketch a speed–time graph for her?

Hydraulic brakes on a car

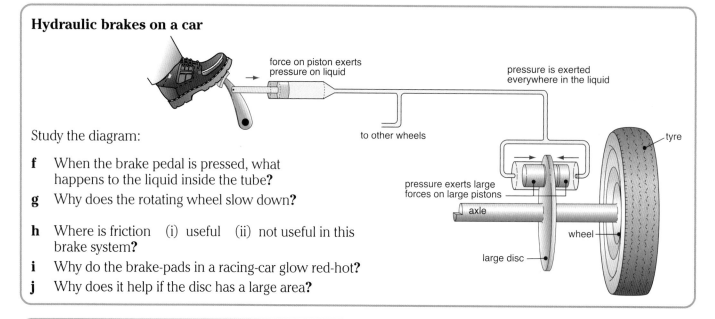

force on piston exerts pressure on liquid

pressure is exerted everywhere in the liquid

to other wheels

pressure exerts large forces on large pistons

axle

large disc

wheel

tyre

Study the diagram:

f When the brake pedal is pressed, what happens to the liquid inside the tube?

g Why does the rotating wheel slow down?

h Where is friction (i) useful (ii) not useful in this brake system?

i Why do the brake-pads in a racing-car glow red-hot?

j Why does it help if the disc has a large area?

Melanie pumps up her **bicycle tyre**. She notices that the pump becomes hot.

k Where did the energy come from to pump up the tyre?

l Explain how the air molecules exert a pressure on the walls of the tyre.

m The air in the tyre was warmed by the pumping. How does this affect the molecules of air?

Space shuttle

When the space shuttle (or a meteorite) enters the Earth's atmosphere, it glows red-hot.

n Explain why. Use the particle theory if you can.

Cycling

The photo shows a racing cyclist.

o Why is he wearing this odd hat?

p Why do some cyclists shave their legs?

q Where does a cyclist find friction
(i) helpful? (ii) not helpful?

r He is holding the handlebars near the centre.
Will this make it easier or harder to turn corners?

Sky-diving

There are 2 forces acting on the parachutist.

s What is the name of the force acting upwards?
t Name the force acting downwards.

u If the man weighs 600 N, and air resistance is
only 500 N, what is the resultant force?
v What happens in this case?

w What happens when his parachute opens?
x Can you explain this, using the particle theory?

Bungee-jumping

Look at this woman jumping off a bridge:

y What is the main force on her?
z Which way is it acting?

As she goes faster, the air starts to exert a force on her.
A What is this force called?
B Which way does it act?

C What stops her hitting the ground?
D Which way does this force act?

The speed–time graph below shows how she falls.

Point A was when she jumped off the bridge.

E At which point (B, C, D, E) is she
moving fastest?
F What is her highest speed?
G At which point has she got most
kinetic energy?

H At which point did she have most
gravitational potential energy?

I Is she moving at point D?
J At which point is the rope stretched
the most?

K Can you predict the shape of the
rest of the graph?

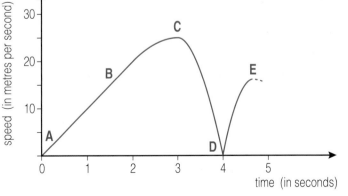

1 The diagram shows a crow-bar. This is a simple machine.

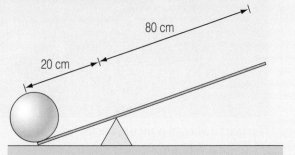

a) Copy the diagram and label the load, the effort and the pivot.
b) Is this crow-bar a force-magnifier or a distance-magnifier?
c) How big a load could you lift with the crow-bar if you pushed down with an effort of 20 N?
d) Explain how you worked this out.

2 The diagram shows an aeroplane. It has 4 forces on it:

The names of the 4 forces are
- the **lift** from the wings,
- the **weight** of the plane,
- the **drag** of the air resistance,
- the **thrust** of the engine.

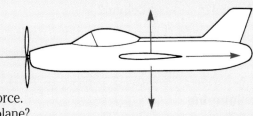

a) Sketch the plane and put the correct label against each force.
b) If the lift is greater than the weight, what happens to the plane?
c) If the thrust is greater than the drag, what happens?

3 The diagram shows a metre rule balanced on a pivot:

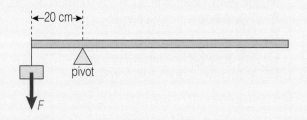

The weight of the rule is 1 N.
a) Where does the weight of the rule act?
b) Re-draw the diagram, showing the weight of the rule.
c) How far is this force from the pivot?
d) What is the value of *F*?
e) What is the total force down on the pivot?
f) What is the force exerted by the pivot on the rule?

4 Jackie has a pair of stilts:

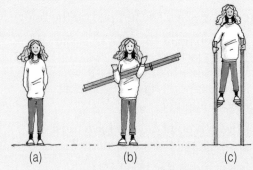

She weighs 400 N and the stilts weigh 100 N.
Each of her shoes has an area of 150 cm².
The bottom of each stilt has an area of 25 cm².
Calculate the pressure on the ground in each of the diagrams:

5 A car with 4 wheels has the tyres at a pressure of 20 N/cm².
Each tyre has an area of 100 cm² in contact with the road.
a) What is the weight of the car?
b) If 1 kg weighs 10 N, what is the mass of the car (in kg)?

Matter

29

Everything around us is a solid, a liquid or a gas.
We ourselves are made of solid, liquid and gas.
These are the 3 states of matter.
But what do the states have in common?
How are they different?

In this topic you'll find out.

What's the matter?

29a

Solids, liquids and gases behave in different ways. We can use ideas about **particles** to explain the differences.

▶ Look at the photos below.
How does each one suggest that matter is made of particles**?**

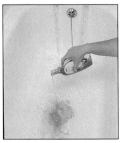

a Blue water**?**

b Hot curry**?**

c Sweet mug**?**

d Lovely smell**?**

Particle tests

Now try these simple tests. For each one, write down what you notice.
What does each one tell you about particles**?** Write down your ideas.
Think about differences between solids, liquids and gases.

Purple shades

1. Take one large purple crystal. Put it in a test-tube.
Add 10 cm³ water. Cork the tube. Carefully shake it to dissolve the crystal.

2. Take 1 cm³ of this solution in another test-tube.
Add 9 cm³ water. Cork the tube. Carefully shake it.

3. Repeat step 2 again and again. Do this until you can't see the pink colour any more.

How many times did you repeat step 2**?**
What does this tell you about the particles in the crystal**?**

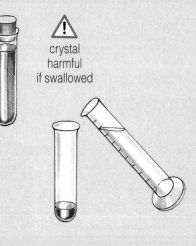

⚠ crystal harmful if swallowed

Lost in spaces?

Measure 25 cm³ sand in a measuring cylinder.
Measure 25 cm³ dried peas in another cylinder.
Predict the total volume when the 2 solids are added together and mixed.

Now mix the 2 solids. Shake the substances well.
Let the mixture settle.
What is the **total** volume**?**

Warm air

Gently warm the tube of air for one minute.
What do you see?
As soon as you stop heating, lift the delivery tube out of the water.

⚠ suck-back

warm

'Dry ice'

Have you seen 'dry ice' being used at pop concerts?
'Dry ice' is solid carbon dioxide.
The solid turns easily to gas. It is stored in pressurised containers.

A **small** volume of solid gives a **large** volume of gas.

e What does this tell you about particles in solids and gases?

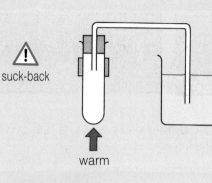

Rising balloons

A balloon rises if it is less dense than the air around it.

f How does the air in a hot-air balloon become less dense than the air outside?
Try to explain your idea by drawing particles.

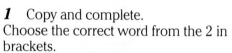

cold air   hot air

heat →   ?

1 Copy and complete.
Choose the correct word from the 2 in brackets.
a) All matter is made of . . . .
   (particles/solids)
b) The particles are very . . . . (small/large)
c) In a gas, the particles are . . . . (more/less) spread out than in a liquid.

2 Soluble aspirin tablets are used to treat headaches.

What happens to the particles in the tablet when it is dropped in water?
Draw pictures to help you to explain.
Use ○ for a water particle.
Use ● for an aspirin particle.

3 This coffee filter collects the coffee grains. Why does the water pass through the filter paper?

4 To make a balloon lighter than air you could fill it with a light gas.
Hydrogen is a light gas.
a) Why isn't hydrogen used to fill passenger balloons?
b) Find out all you can about the Hindenburg.

Things to do

Particles on the move

▶ Draw 3 diagrams to show how you think particles are arranged in a solid, a liquid and a gas.

How do your diagrams explain that:

a solids are hard to compress (squash)?
b gases are easy to compress?
c liquids can be poured?
d gases are the shape of their container?

Solids, liquids and gases are here

Materials **expand** when they get hot.
They **contract** when they cool down.

e What does *expand* mean?
f What does *contract* mean?
g When a solid expands, what do you think happens to the particles?

▶ Look at your answers to **e**, **f** and **g**.
Use these to help you with the photo questions.

h Why is mercury used in thermometers?

i Railway tracks contain small gaps. Why do they have these?

j Boiling water should not be poured into a cold glass. Why not?

k Concrete roads have gaps between sections. Why are these filled with tar?

l Warming the jam jar lid may help to remove it. Why?

Watching for movement

Do particles move? Try some of these tests to find out.

A blue move?
Before you do this test, predict what will happen.

Put a few blue crystals in the bottom of a beaker.
Carefully pour water on the top.
Do not shake or stir.
Leave the beaker for a few days.
Draw pictures to show what happens.

Do you think particles move?
Write down or draw what you think happens to the particles.

Use some of these words to explain what happens.

dissolve   move
particles   spread
blue   mix
water   collide

Smoke signals?
Your teacher will show you this experiment.

When fumes from the acid and ammonia meet, white smoke forms.

What do you think will happen in this experiment?
Predict *exactly* what you will see.

Your teacher will do this experiment.
Try to explain what you see.

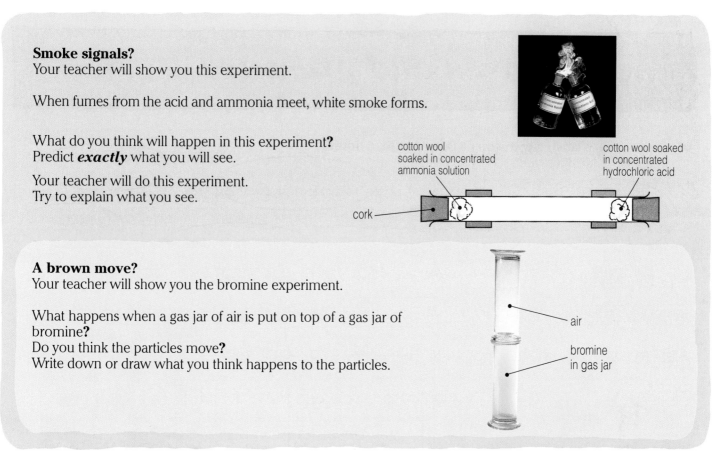

cotton wool
soaked in concentrated
ammonia solution

cotton wool soaked
in concentrated
hydrochloric acid

cork

A brown move?
Your teacher will show you the bromine experiment.

What happens when a gas jar of air is put on top of a gas jar of bromine?
Do you think the particles move?
Write down or draw what you think happens to the particles.

air

bromine
in gas jar

Diffusion

Liquid and gas particles can move and mix. They do this without being stirred or shaken. This is called **diffusion**.

Have you ever smelt freshly baked bread?
Particles of gas are released from the bread. They **diffuse** through the air. You can smell the bread throughout the room.

The *Watching for movement* tests tell you about *rates* of diffusion too.

m Which diffuses faster, a gas or a liquid? Why?

---

1 Copy and complete:
a) These are the particles in a . . . .

b) These are the particles in a . . . .

c) These are the particles in a . . . .

2 Robert Brown was a Scottish scientist. He studied pollen grains in water. Find out about what he saw. This is called Brownian motion.

3 Helium is a lighter gas than air. Gas particles can diffuse through balloon rubber. This is why balloons go down.

Which balloon do you think will go down first? Why?

Things to do

Gases and pressure

▶ Copy out each label. Say whether it is for a **solid**, a **liquid** or a **gas**. (Clue: there are 2 labels for each!)

The particles are very close together. They are in a regular pattern.

The particles move about quickly and in all directions.

The particles are far apart and arranged randomly.

The particles do not move about. They vibrate.

The particles are close together but random.

The particles move about.

▶ Look at the 2 labels you have chosen for gases. These tell you about **gas pressure**.

Gas pressure . . .

. . . keeps a balloon blown up.

. . . an area of high pressure in the south.

. . . tells us about the weather.

. . . gives us a comfy bike ride!

Gas pressure

What causes the pressure? Particles help us to understand.

Think about gas inside a balloon.
The particles move around very quickly.
They move in all directions. Some particles hit each other.
Others hit the wall of the balloon. Those that hit the wall give a force on each unit of area of the balloon. This is called the **pressure** of the gas.
The more often particles hit the wall, the greater the pressure.
The harder they hit the wall, the greater the pressure.

Think about gases

Make some predictions. Discuss these in your group.

1   Think of a gas in a closed box. What happens if you heat the gas? Do you think the pressure will increase or decrease? Try to explain using the idea of particles.

2   Think of a gas in a syringe. The plunger can move in and out. What happens to the plunger if you heat the gas? Try to explain using the idea of particles.

Check your predictions with your teacher.

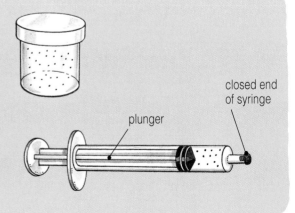

plunger

closed end of syringe

Moving gases

Your teacher will show you an experiment using a porous pot.
The porous pot lets gas particles (molecules) through its walls.
Your teacher will put some natural gas into the beaker.
The gas is lighter than air.
Think about the movement of gas molecules.

Try to explain what you see.
Use your ideas about gas pressure and diffusion.

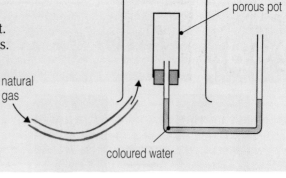
porous pot

natural gas

coloured water

Gases into liquids

Gases can be turned into liquids. One way to do this is to put the gas in a pressurised container. We say the gas is **compressed** or stored **under pressure**.

a   Why does *compressing* a gas turn it to a liquid?
Use particles to explain.

You have probably seen tankers like the one in the photograph:
This one is used to carry liquid nitrogen.

b   Why are gases stored and transported as liquids?

Liquid nitrogen is very useful. It is very cold.
Lots of foods are frozen by spraying them with liquid nitrogen.

c   Why do we freeze foods?

d   Are frozen foods good for you? Write about your ideas.

Propane and butane can also be stored as liquids.

e   What are these gases used for?

f   What are the dangers of these gases?

g   Why does the pressure in a butane cylinder fall when the temperature falls?

A pressurised tanker

Freezing foods

---

1   Copy and complete:
Particles in a gas . . . . quickly in . . . . directions. When they hit the . . . . of a container this is called the gas . . . . This is the . . . . on each unit of area. Gas particles move more . . . . when they are heated. As the gas is heated in the container, the pressure . . . .

2

WARNING Contains flammable solvents.

Pressurised container: protect from sunlight and do not expose to temperatures exceeding 50°C. Do not pierce or burn, even after use. Do not spray on a naked flame or any incandescent material. Ensure adequate ventilation when in use. Keep out of reach of children.

Why shouldn't you put this near to heat?

3   Look at these boiling points of gases that are in the air.

xenon	−108°C	krypton	−153°C
argon	−186°C	nitrogen	−196°C
oxygen	−183°C	helium	−269°C
	neon	−246°C	

To collect the gases, air is cooled so it becomes liquid. The liquid air is slowly warmed so the gases boil off.

a)   Which 2 gases have the closest boiling points?

b)   When liquid air is warmed, which boils off first – oxygen, argon or nitrogen?

c)   What is this method of separating called?

d)   Which gas is the most common in the air?

e)   Which gas is needed for burning?

f)   Name 3 gases with similar properties. (Clue: use the Periodic Table.)

Things to do

Energy for a change

Water is usually found as a liquid. But water can be a solid (ice) or a gas (steam).
Ice, water and steam are the same chemical substance (H_2O).
When water turns into ice or steam we say it is **changing state**.

> Sketch the pictures of the 3 states of water. Write a label next
> to each arrow. Choose the correct label from this list:

boil (or evaporate)   **melt**   **freeze**   **condense**

a At what temperature does water boil?

b At what temperatures does ice melt?

distillation is evaporation + condensation

Is this true? Explain.

Energy and the water cycle

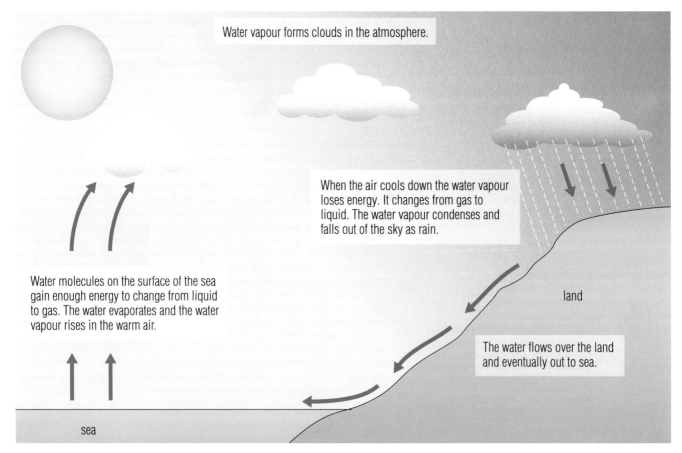

Water vapour forms clouds in the atmosphere.

When the air cools down the water vapour loses energy. It changes from gas to liquid. The water vapour condenses and falls out of the sky as rain.

Water molecules on the surface of the sea gain enough energy to change from liquid to gas. The water evaporates and the water vapour rises in the warm air.

land

The water flows over the land and eventually out to sea.

sea

c What provides the energy that drives the water cycle?

Feeling cool?

Dip your finger into water.
Dip the same finger of the other hand into alcohol.
Hold your fingers out in front of you.

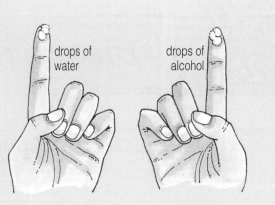
drops of water   drops of alcohol

d Which liquid cools your skin the most?
e Which liquid evaporates faster?
f Try to explain these results using the idea of moving particles.
g What happens to the temperature of a liquid as it evaporates?
h You have thermometers, rubber bands, paper tissues, beakers and a stop-clock.
  How can you use this apparatus to find out which liquid evaporates fastest – alcohol, water or propanone?

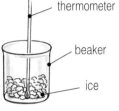
thermometer

beaker

ice

Hassan studied some ice melting.
He stirred crushed ice in a beaker.
He took the temperature of the ice every 2 minutes.
These are his results:

Time (minutes)	0	2	4	6	8	10	12	14	16	18	20
Temperature (°C)	-4	-2	0	0	0	0	0	0	0	2	5

i At what temperature did the ice melt?
j Ice melts when it is heated. Where did the heat come from in this experiment?
k Why didn't the temperature rise between 4 and 16 minutes? Explain what happens to the particles.

Salt lowers the freezing point of water.

l Why do we put salt on icy roads in winter?

---

1 Copy and complete using **heat** or **cool**:
a) To turn a solid to a liquid you need to . . . . it.
b) To turn a liquid to a gas you need to . . . . it.
c) To turn a gas to a liquid you need to . . . . it.
d) To turn a liquid to a solid you need to . . . . it.

2 Use the words from the box to describe
a) melting point   b) boiling point.

> solid   liquid   gas   temperature

3 Use the words below to help explain the water cycle in terms of movement of particles.

> evaporate   sea   Sun   cloud
> rain   condense

4 Look at this heating curve for a solid substance X:

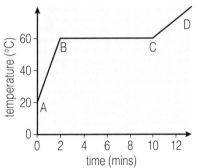

a) What is the state of X from:
  i) A to B?   ii) B to C?   iii) C to D?
b) What is the melting point of X?
c) X is being heated. Why does the temperature stay steady between B and C?
d) What do you think happens if heating carries on?

Things to do

167

Dissolving

Do you like drinking tea?
There's a lot of science in action when you make tea.

▶ Look at what you do:

Boiling the water.   Brewing the tea.   Adding milk and sugar.

Write about the particles in each step shown above.
Where are they? What is happening to them?
Start with the water particles in the kettle. Finish with the particles
in your cup of milky sweet tea.
Try to use some or all of these words and phrases:

moving slowly	*moving more quickly*	*steam*	*diffuse*	*soluble*
insoluble	*close together*	*far apart*	*dissolve*	*mix*

Sugar dissolves in a hot cup of tea. It dissolves in the water.
It makes a **solution**. Sugar is **soluble**.
In a solution the substance which dissolves is the **solute**. Sugar is the **solute**.
The water dissolves the sugar.
The water is the **solvent**.

solute   +   solvent   ⟶   solution

Dissolving quickly

Think about all the things that affect dissolving.
How could you get a sugar cube to dissolve as
quickly as possible?

a Make a list of your
ideas.

b Explain each idea
in terms of particles.

Making a solution

Emma adds the salt to the water
in the beaker.

5.5 g of salt

water

c When all the salt has
dissolved, what is the
reading on the balance?
Explain this using the
idea of particles.

d How can Emma get
the solid salt back?

In most solutions the solvent is water. But other substances can be solvents.

Have you ever had any clothes dry-cleaned?
Dry cleaning uses solvents without water in them.
These are called non-aqueous solvents.

e What type of stains can dry-cleaning remove?

f Why don't we dry-clean **all** our clothes?

Nail varnish remover is another non-aqueous solvent.

g What is its chemical name?

MADE IN RUSSIA
57% VISCOSE/Вискоза
43% ACETATE/Ацетат
LINING/Подкладка
100% POLYESTER/
Полизфир

M20627

PROFESSIONAL
DRY CLEAN
ONLY

Clean nails

Paint some nail varnish on a glass slide.
Leave it to dry for a few minutes.
Test the 3 solvents your teacher will give you.
Which is best at removing the varnish?

Some solutes are very soluble in a solvent but they may be **in**soluble in another solvent.
They have different **solubilities** in different solvents.

A stain remover

Plan an investigation on solvents.
Which solvent is best at removing stains?

Your teacher will give you some substances which stain.
Examples could be:

  ball-point pen   felt-tip pen   grease

    paint   grass   coffee   tea

      orange juice   tomato sauce

Ask your teacher to check your plan.
Then do the investigation.

⚠ Some solvents are very flammable. Make sure there are no Bunsens alight in the lab.

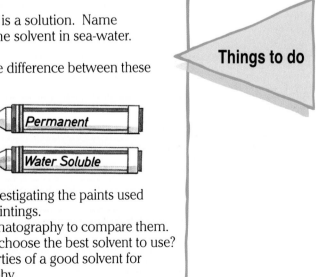

1 Copy and complete:
a) A substance which . . . . is soluble.
b) A substance which does not . . . . is insoluble.
c) Solute + solvent → . . . .
d) Solvents without . . . . are non-aqueous.
e) Solutes have different . . . . in different solvents.

2 Which of these are soluble in water?
a) sand
b) salt
c) chalk
d) butter
e) wax
f) sugar
g) detergent

3 Sea-water is a solution. Name a solute and the solvent in sea-water.

4 What's the difference between these felt-tip pens?

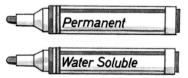

Permanent

Water Soluble

5 Tom is investigating the paints used in some oil paintings.
He uses chromatography to compare them.
How does he choose the best solvent to use?
List the properties of a good solvent for chromatography.

Things to do

▶ Nazia makes a solution from 4 g of salt and 100 g of water. Describe 2 ways she could make a solution which is *half* as concentrated.

Some solutions contain only *a little solute* in *a lot of solvent*. We say the solutions are **dilute**.
Some solutions contain *a lot of solute* in only *a little solvent*. We say the solutions are **concentrated**.

What happens if we heat a concentrated solution?

As more and more solvent evaporates, the solution becomes more and more concentrated.
Eventually it cannot become any more concentrated.
If more solvent evaporates, solute comes out of the solution.
We see solid forming. The solution is **saturated**.

A **saturated** solution is one in which no more solute will dissolve (at that temperature).

Salt deposits as sea water evaporates

Plotting solubility curves

The amount of a substance that can dissolve in a certain amount of solvent (at that temperature) is called the **solubility** of the substance.

We can measure the solubility of a substance at different temperatures. If the information is plotted on a graph, it makes a **solubility curve**.

▶ Use the information in the table to plot a solubility curve for potassium chloride:

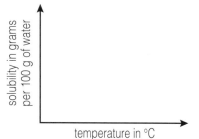

Making a solution

a What is the solubility of potassium chloride at 45°C?

b What is the lowest temperature at which 36 g of potassium chloride dissolves in 100 g of water?

c At 80°C, how much potassium chloride dissolves in 1 kg (1000 g) of water?

d At 25°C, how much potassium chloride dissolves in 20 g of water?

e At 40°C, how much potassium chloride dissolves in 28 g of water?

f What happens to the solubility of potassium chloride as the temperature increases?

Temperature in °C	Solubility in grams per 100 g of water
0	28.0
10	31.0
20	34.5
30	37.5
40	40.0
50	43.0
60	45.5
70	48.5
80	51.0
90	54.0
100	56.5

This table shows how the solubility of potassium chloride changes with temperature.

Testing solubility

Plan a test to see which compound is the most soluble in water.

Think about:

- How will you make this a fair test?
- How will you make your solutions saturated?
- How will you measure how much solid dissolves?
- How will you make your results reliable?
- What apparatus will you use?
- How will you record your results?

Ask your teacher to check your plan.
You can then collect some compounds to test.

Which is the most soluble?

Copper sulphate is very soluble.

I think sodium chloride is more soluble.

Solubility patterns

Scientists have measured the solubility of lots of compounds.
Some patterns can be seen. Look at the solubility table:
Use this table to work out answers to **g** to **l**.

Are these compounds soluble or insoluble in water:

g copper chloride?
h potassium carbonate?
i magnesium nitrate?
j lead sulphate?
k iron carbonate?
l ammonium sulphide?

Solubility Table

- All sodium, potassium and ammonium compounds — are soluble
- All nitrates — are soluble
- All chlorides — are soluble (except $AgCl$, $PbCl_2$)
- All sulphates — are soluble (except Ag_2SO_4, $BaSO_4$, $CaSO_4$, $PbSO_4$)
- All carbonates — are insoluble (except Na_2CO_3, K_2CO_3, $(NH_4)_2CO_3$)
- All sulphides — are insoluble (except Na_2S, K_2S, $(NH_4)_2S$)

Things to do

1 Explain the meanings of each of these words or phrases:
a) solution
b) saturated solution
c) solubility
d) solubility curve.

2 At 60°C, 40 g of copper sulphate dissolves in 100 g of water to make a saturated solution.
a) At 60°C, how much will dissolve in 250 g of water?
b) At 60°C, how much will dissolve in 46 g of water?
c) Why is the solubility of solids in water normally given only for temperatures between 0°C–100°C?

3 A hot, saturated solution of potassium nitrate in water is cooled to room temperature. Describe what you would see. (Use the graph for question 4 to help you.)

4 Look at these solubility curves:

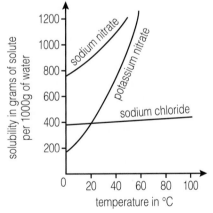

a) Which substance is the most soluble at room temperature?
b) Which substance is the least soluble at room temperature? (Explain your answer carefully!)
c) Which substance has a solubility which changes only a little with temperature?

Questions

1 Name some things in your body which are
a) solid b) liquid c) gas.

2 Dan's teacher drew some particle diagrams for his class.
But the labels got muddled.
Copy out the diagrams. Choose the right label to write under each diagram.

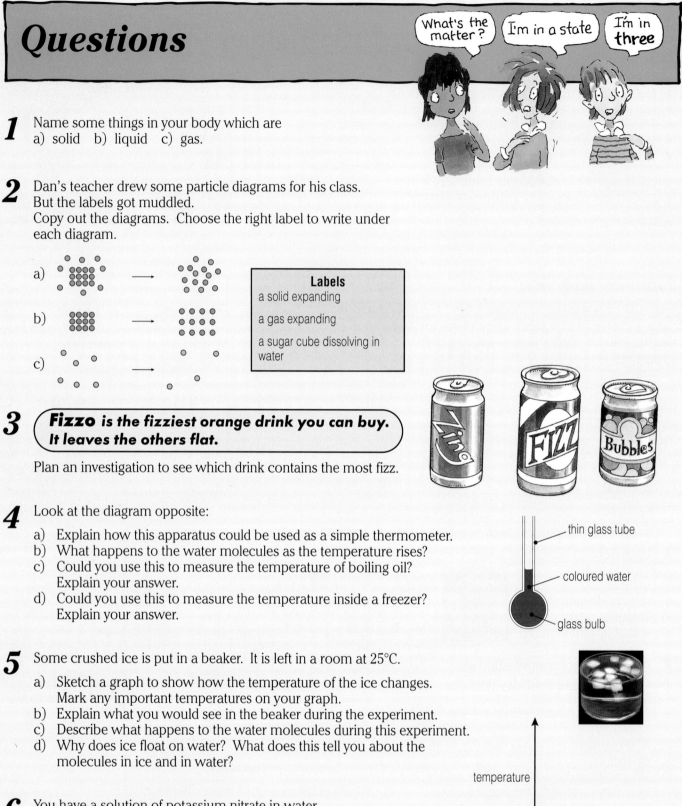

Labels

a solid expanding

a gas expanding

a sugar cube dissolving in water

3 **Fizzo** *is the fizziest orange drink you can buy.*
It leaves the others flat.

Plan an investigation to see which drink contains the most fizz.

4 Look at the diagram opposite:

a) Explain how this apparatus could be used as a simple thermometer.
b) What happens to the water molecules as the temperature rises?
c) Could you use this to measure the temperature of boiling oil?
   Explain your answer.
d) Could you use this to measure the temperature inside a freezer?
   Explain your answer.

thin glass tube

coloured water

glass bulb

5 Some crushed ice is put in a beaker. It is left in a room at 25°C.

a) Sketch a graph to show how the temperature of the ice changes.
   Mark any important temperatures on your graph.
b) Explain what you would see in the beaker during the experiment.
c) Describe what happens to the water molecules during this experiment.
d) Why does ice float on water? What does this tell you about the
   molecules in ice and in water?

temperature

time

6 You have a solution of potassium nitrate in water.
The solution is saturated.
How can you find out the solubility of potassium nitrate at room temperature?
What apparatus will you need? Describe what you will do.
What measurements will you make?
Show how you will calculate the solubility.

Variation

30

We inherit many of our features from our parents.
They are passed on from one generation to the next.

The same but different

Look at the kittens in the picture:
They are all from the same litter.

a In what ways do you think they look alike**?**

b In what ways do you think they look different**?**

▶ Look around at the people in your class.
   They have a lot in common: they are all human for a start!
   But they also have features that are different.
   Make a list of some of these differences.

Why do we look like we do?

We get some of our features from our parents. We **inherit** them.
Other features do not come from our parents.
These features are caused by the way we lead our life.
We call these features **environmental**.

Can you roll your tongue like the girl in the photograph**?**

You can't learn how to do it. You have either inherited it from your
parents or you haven't.

The soccer player in the photograph has a lot of natural ability.
Do you think that this is inherited or environmental**?**
But to be a top-class player, strength, agility and stamina are needed.
Do you think that these are inherited or environmental**?**

▶ Copy out the following list of features.
   Write (i) after those that you think are inherited,
   and   (e) after those that you think are environmental.

shape of nose	neat writing	freckles	hair colour
hair length	scars	skill at languages	an accent
eye colour	good at sport	blood group	size of feet

How do you measure up?

Nobody's the same, we are all unique!
Collect the following information about yourself and others in your class:

eye colour   height   left-handed *or* right-handed   shoe size

length of index finger   hair colour   tongue rolling   ear lobes

Record your findings.
Some things vary **gradually**.

c   Draw a bar-chart to show the number of people in your class with different length index fingers. What do you find**?**

Other things are more **clear-cut**. For instance there are only a few different types of eye colour.

d   Draw a bar-chart to show the number of people in your class with different colour eyes. What do you find**?**

▶ Look at the graph of the height of some pupils:

e   How many children are less than 160 cm**?**

f   What is the most common height**?**

g   Do you think that the variation shown on the graph is gradual or clear-cut**?**

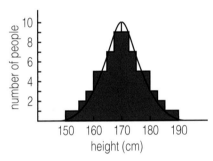

▶ Look at the graph of the hair colour of some pupils:

h   What is the most common hair colour in the class**?**

i   How is this graph different from the graph for height**?**

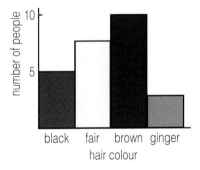

Things to do

1   Copy and complete:
We . . . . many features from our parents. Other things, like being able to ride a bike, we . . . . during our lifetime. We say that they are due to the . . . .
Some variation, like height, is . . . . Other variation, such as eye colour, is . . . .

2   Libby has just come home from 2 weeks in Majorca.
Do you think her sun-tan is inherited?
Explain your answer.

3   Mike says "I think red hair and being good at sport are both inherited."
Do you agree or disagree? Give your reasons.

4   Look at the picture of a litter of puppies:
a)   What features have the puppies inherited from their mother?
b)   What features have the puppies inherited from their father?

A design for life

Have you ever heard someone say of a new baby, "Isn't she like her father?" or "Doesn't he have his mother's eyes?"

What things do you think you have inherited from your parents?

What's a chromosome?

How do we inherit things from our parents?

The **instructions** for designing a new baby are found in 2 places:

* the egg cell of the mother, and
* the sperm cell of the father.

a Which part of these cells do you think contains these instructions?

Most cells in your body contain a nucleus.
Each nucleus contains **chromosomes**.
It is the chromosomes that carry the instructions.

▶ Look at the photo:

b What do the chromosomes look like?

c Are they all the same size and shape?

d How many are there?

In most human cells there are 46 chromosomes.
We can put them into 23 pairs that are identical.

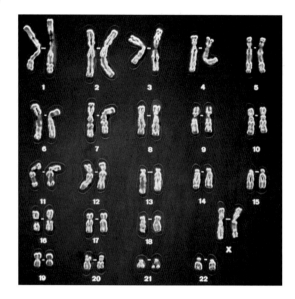

Halving and doubling

When a sperm cell or an egg cell is made, the chromosomes in each pair split up.

e So how many chromosomes will there be in the sperm or egg now?
Do you remember what happens when a sperm fertilises an egg?

▶ Look at the diagram:

f How many chromosomes does a fertilised egg contain?

g Where have these chromosomes come from?

h What do you think would happen at fertilisation if the sperm and the egg each contained 46 chromosomes?

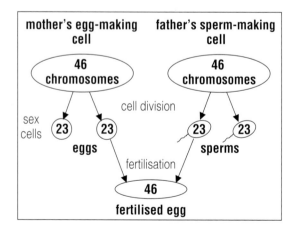

Looking at chromosomes

Scientists can make slides of human chromosomes.
Your teacher will give you a sheet showing what these
chromosomes look like.

- Count the number of chromosomes.
- Cut out your chromosomes and count them again to make sure
  you haven't lost any.
- Arrange them on a sheet of paper. Start with the largest and end
  with the smallest.
- Arrange your chromosomes in pairs according to size and
  pattern of banding.
- Stick down your chromosomes neatly in their pairs.

i Are these chromosomes from a female or a male?

j How do you know?

k What do you think the bands on each chromosome might be?

Genes

Genes contain the instructions that we inherit.
Genes control certain features like eye colour.

▶ Look at the diagram:

l How many genes do you think there are for each feature?

m Where are they found?

n What do you notice about the position of genes on a pair of
chromosomes?
Each band on a chromosome represents one gene.

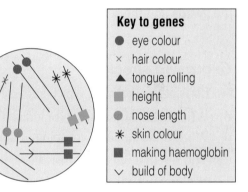

Key to genes

- ● eye colour
- × hair colour
- ▲ tongue rolling
- ■ height
- ● nose length
- ✳ skin colour
- ■ making haemoglobin
- ∨ build of body

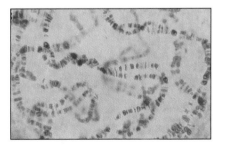

Things to do

1 Copy and complete:
Inside the nucleus of each cell there are
thread-like shapes, called . . . .
These are made up of . . . .
These . . . . contain instructions to control
how the . . . . works.
They also contain information which is . . . .
from one generation to the next.

2 How many chromosomes are there in a
human sperm or a human egg?
How many are there in other human cells?
Why do you think these numbers are
different?

3 Where are genes found?
What do genes do?
Genes are made of the chemical called DNA.
Try to find out what DNA stands for.

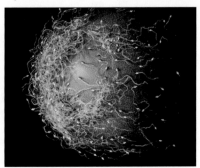

What's in a name?

What do the ox-eye daisy, the dog daisy and marguerite have in common?
The answer is that they are all the same plant.
But they have different names in different parts of Britain.

a Why do you think that using 'common names' can be confusing?

Well if you wanted to describe a particular plant or animal to someone in another country, you would be speaking in different languages.

Luckily we have a **binomial system** of naming living things.
This gives every living thing *2* names: the first name is the **genus** and the second name is the **species**.

For instance, Homo sapiens is the **scientific name** for a human.

b What do we mean by a species?

A species is a very similar group of individuals that can breed together and produce fertile offspring.
For example, all domestic dogs belong to the same species.
They may look different, but they can mate and give birth to cross-breeds that are perfectly healthy.

Grouping species

▶ Look at the diagram, which shows how we **classify** the grizzly bear.

c What is the largest group of individuals in the diagram?

d What is the smallest grouping in the diagram called?

Can you see that we can classify living things on the basis of their **shared** features?

e Use the diagram to list the groups in order of size. Start with the smallest and end up with the largest group.

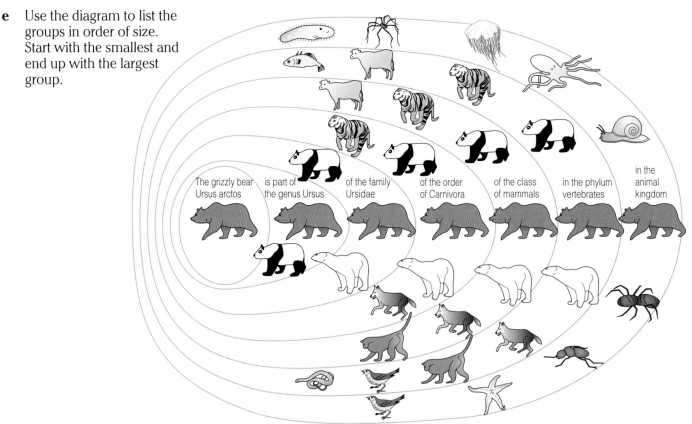

The grizzly bear Ursus arctos | is part of the genus Ursus | of the family Ursidae | of the order of Carnivora | of the class of mammals | in the phylum vertebrates | in the animal kingdom

The name game

This game will help you revise invertebrate classification.

Choose a partner and sit opposite each other.

You will both be given 16 cards each with a picture and description of an invertebrate that lives in freshwater.

Lay out your 16 cards face-up on the table in front of you.

Your partner keeps his or her cards hidden and picks out **one** card, looks at it and places it in an envelope – so you don't know which it is.

You now have to ask questions based upon the pictures and descriptions to try and find out which invertebrate is in the envelope.

But your partner is only allowed to answer 'yes' or 'no'.

Write down the question that you ask each time.

Turn over the cards that you eliminate with each question.

Eventually you will identify the invertebrate chosen by your partner.

Now swap roles and see how many questions your partner needs to ask to identify the invertebrate that you choose.

The person with the **fewest** questions wins **'The name game!'**

Things to do

1   Copy and complete:
A group of organisms that can mate and produce . . . .
offspring is called a . . . .
The study of how we put living things into groups is called . . . .
It uses the . . . . system by giving every living thing 2 names.
The first is called the . . . . name and the second the . . . . name.
We classify living things on the basis of their . . . . features.

2   The Arthropods are a phylum of jointed-legged animals.
a)   Can you name the 4 main classes?
b)   Give an example of an animal from each of these classes.

3   The Plants are classified into 4 main groups.
a)   Can you name each of these groups?
b)   Give an example of a plant from each group.

4   The vertebrates make up one phylum.
a)   What feature do all vertebrates have?
b)   Name the 5 main classes of vertebrates.
c)   Give an example of an animal from each of these classes.
d)   To which class of vertebrates do each of the following belong:
i) a turtle?   ii) a bat?   iii) a whale?
iv) a salamander?   v) a snake?

To which class of Arthropods do these belong?

179

30d *Pick and mix*

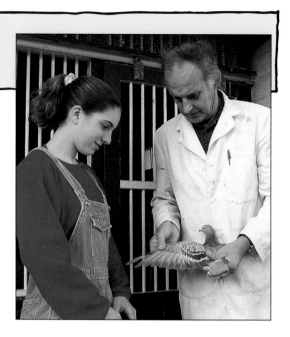

Vicki's dad keeps racing pigeons.
She helps to look after them.
They are related to wild pigeons, but have been specially bred.
They have to fly long distances but always return home.

a What features do you think have been bred into racing pigeons?

Selective breeding means that we breed in the features that we want and breed out the features that we don't want.

▶ Write down a list of animals and plants that humans have selectively bred.
Why do you think humans have selectively bred these animals and plants?

Calypso fruit

A new type of fruit has been discovered on a tropical island.
It has an amazing taste, but only when it is just ripe.
The skin is covered with hairs and it is difficult to remove.
It has a bright orange colour that often attracts birds.
The number of its seeds varies and they are very bitter.
It is said to be very good for the digestion since it contains a lot of fibre.
The calypso fruits are hard to pick because the stem has lots of thorns.

b Draw a diagram of what you think the calypso fruit looks like.

c What features would you try to breed out?

d What features would you keep?

e What would your calypso fruit look like after selective breeding?

This little piggy . . .

Our modern pig is descended from the wild pig.

▶ Look at the photos:

Bacon pig

Wild pig

f Which features do you think have been bred into the modern pig?

g Which features do you think have been bred out of it?

h Do you think the modern pig could survive in the wild?
Give your reasons.

Supercow!

Farmers can now breed better cattle.
New breeds of cattle produce more milk and more beef.

Artificial insemination means that sperm can be taken from the best bulls and put directly into the best cows.
This means that the farmer no longer has to keep bulls of his own.

i Why do you think this is an advantage to the farmer?

Eggs from the best cows can be removed and fertilised with bull sperm in a test-tube.
The fertilised egg is then put back into the mother cow.
These are called **embryo transplants**.

j What do you think are the advantages to breeders of:
  i) artificial insemination?
  ii) embryo transplants?

k Why do you think it is important to keep alive some of the old-fashioned breeds of cattle?

In your groups, discuss whether you think that artificial insemination and embryo transplants should be used on farm animals.

Things to do

1 Make a list of 5 animals or plants that you think have been 'improved' by selective breeding. For each one, say how you think this is useful to humans.

2 A lot of cereals originally came from the Middle East.
What features do you think have been bred into varieties that are grown in Britain?

3 What features do you think have been bred into these dogs:
a) pekingese?   b) sheep dog?
c) bloodhound?

4 Humans have selectively bred modern varieties of wheat from wild wheat.
These have greater yield, improved disease resistance and ripen over a shorter time.
How do you think these 3 features have helped the farmer?

30e

Biology at Work

The Human Genome Project

The Human Genome Project is a six-billion dollar venture involving over 1000 scientists from 50 countries around the world. Its aim is to trace every single human gene and find its particular position on a chromosome.

a   What is a gene and what does it do?

Genes are found on chromosomes.

b   What are chromosomes?

c   Where are chromosomes found?

In June 2000, the human genome was completed:

3 billion 'chemical letters' that spell out all the human genes.

Scientists will be able to use the information to understand how people are affected by certain diseases and target early treatment. Cancer scientists have begun to catalogue the DNA changes in cancer cells in the hope of developing totally new treatments.

d   How do cancers form in the body?

e   How do cancer cells spread through the body?

f   Give 2 ways in which cancers are currently treated?

The Human Genome Project will help create new drugs to treat heart disease, immune disorders, muscular dystrophy, birth defects and degenerative nervous diseases.

g   Find out more about some of these diseases.

h   Use the internet to find out more about the Human Genome Project. Your teacher can give you some internet links.

Dr John Sulston, director of the Sanger Centre where the British genome work was based

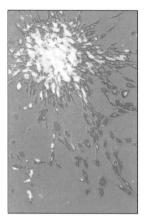

Cancer cells breaking away from a tumour.

In vitro fertilisation (IVF)

Explain how each of the following could stop a couple having children:

i   The man cannot make enough sperms.

j   The woman's egg tubes can become blocked.

In vitro fertilisation can often help these couples.

k   What is meant by fertilisation?

'In vitro' means 'in glass'.

l   Why do you think this technique is called IVF?

First the woman is injected with hormones to make her produce eggs.

m   How do you think the eggs are removed from her body?

The eggs are then kept in a solution containing food and oxygen at the correct temperature.

n   Why do you think this is?

Look at the diagram:

o   Write a paragraph to explain exactly how IVF is carried out.

Sometimes more embryos form than can be used.

Many people think that it is wrong to destroy these extra embryos.

p   What do you think? Write about your thoughts.

Sometimes these extra embryos are frozen. They can then be used later if the first embryos do not grow.

q   Do you think that it is right to do this? Write about your thoughts.

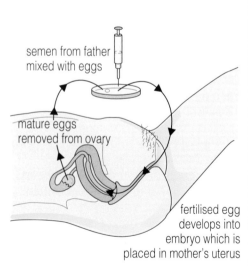

semen from father mixed with eggs

mature eggs removed from ovary

fertilised egg develops into embryo which is placed in mother's uterus

The GM food debate

Genetically modified (GM) food in the form of soya products, tomato purée or vegetarian cheese has probably been eaten by most people already.

What are GM foods?
Genetic engineering has allowed sections of DNA to be removed from some plants and transferred into other plant cells.

r What chemicals are used to remove and transfer this DNA?

GM foods – the benefits
- **Solving global hunger** – crops can be developed with the genes that give them tolerance of drought, frost and salty soil.

s How does this help solve food shortage?

- **Environmentally friendly** – genetic modification can give crops resistance to insect pests, weeds and diseases.

t How can this help the environment?

Crops can be developed that are able to take up nitrogen better.

u How can this help the environment?

- **Consumer benefits** – GM food can be produced with better flavour, better keeping qualities and which need fewer additives.

v How do these qualities help suppliers and consumers?

GM foods – the concerns
Opposition to the increased use of GM foods has come from the following areas:

- **Environmental safety** – there are worries that GM crops may become successful weeds and transfer their genes to related plants.

w How might a plant that develops insect-resistant genes become a weed?

- **Food safety** – there are concerns that the proteins that GM food genes can produce could be transferred to microbes in the human intestine.

x How might this prove to be a threat to human health?

- **Changes in farming structure** – there has been a trend, over the past decades, towards larger more intensive farms.

y Why might the production of GM foods favour wealthy farmers?

- **Biodiversity** – the control of plant breeding could result in fewer varieties of plant species being available to farmers.

z Why could the reduced use of old varieties and their wild relatives put more plants in danger of attack by pests and diseases?

- **Animal health** – there is increasing resistance to any developments in the use of farm animals that could affect their welfare.

A Either research further aspects of the benefits and concerns of GM foods on the internet or set up a debate with groups arguing these benefits and concerns about this new biotechnology.

Greenpeace activists destroying a GM trial crop

Questions

1 What features do you think that you have inherited from
a) your mother?　b) your father?
If you have a sister or brother, have they inherited the same features?

2 Bob and Baz are identical twins:
What features have they inherited from their parents?
What features are the result of their environment?

3 Some pupils did a survey on the size of foxglove fruits.
Here are their results:

Length of fruit (mm)	20	21	22	23	24	25	26	27	28	29
Number collected	4	6	14	22	30	26	18	12	12	3

a) Draw a bar-chart of their results.
b) What sort of variation do you think this shows?

4 Cloning involves taking some pieces of tissue from a parent plant
and growing them in sterile conditions in nutrient agar.
a) Why will the cloned plants be 'genetically identical' to the parent?
b) Why are the clones grown in sterile conditions?
c) Explain how plants grown in this way can:
(i) be produced quickly　ii) be free from disease　(iii) have the
'good' qualities of the parent plant, e.g. disease-resistance.
d) Find out and write about any examples of animal cloning.

5 Breeding racehorses is a million-pound industry.
What sort of features do you think would be bred into a champion racehorse?

6 If animals of 2 different species mate they produce a **hybrid**.
The tigon resulted when a tiger and a lion mated in captivity:
a) What do you think were the parents of a leopon and a zeedonk?
b) Invent your own animal from 2 different species and draw it.
c) Hybrids are usually sterile (they cannot produce offspring).
Why do you think that the survival of some species would be
threatened if they bred with other species in the wild?

tigon

7 Look at the table of 2 breeds of sheep:

Feature	Welsh Mountain breed	Border Leicester breed
adult mass (kg)	30–32	73–77
number of lambs born per female (ewe)	1	2
temperament	wild	docile
fleece per ewe (kg)	1	3
growth rate	slow	fast

a) What features do you think have been bred into the Border Leicester?
b) How do these make it a successful sheep?
c) Hill farmers often cross Welsh Mountain ewes with Border Leicester rams. Why do you think this is?

Using chemical reactions

31

Chemical reactions keep you alive.
Today you'll probably be eating food made by chemical reactions.
Reactions may also be keeping you warm.

Some reactions are so powerful they can put a rocket into space . . . .

What a change!

What can you remember about **chemical changes?**
a   Write down 3 things that might happen in a chemical change.

Scientists talk about 2 kinds of changes –
chemical changes and **physical changes**.
In a **chemical change** a new substance is made.
It's not easy to get the substance you started with back again.
We say the change is **irreversible**.
In a **physical change** no new substance is made.
We say the change is **reversible**.

A fire burning is a chemical change

▶ Look at the photos of some changes.
For each one, say if you think it is a chemical change, or a
physical change. Explain why.

b

c

d

e   **f**

g

h   **i**   **j**

When a new substance is made, a chemical reaction must happen.
This is a **chemical change**.
The new substance is called a **product**.
You have seen lots of chemical reactions already.
Do you remember burning magnesium**?**

| magnesium + oxygen $\longrightarrow$ magnesium oxide |
| 2 Mg + O$_2$ $\longrightarrow$ 2 MgO |

▶ Copy and complete these word equations for reactions:

copper + ... $\longrightarrow$ copper oxide

iron + ... $\longrightarrow$ iron chloride

When a substance changes state it changes into a different form.
It may look different but it is still the same substance.
This is a **physical change**.

Try balancing these symbol equations:

.... Cu + O$_2$ $\longrightarrow$ .... CuO

.... Fe + ... Cl$_2$ $\longrightarrow$ .... FeCl$_3$

Does the mass change?

Do you think **mass** changes ... during a physical change?
... during a chemical change?
Predict what your conclusions will be before you do each test.

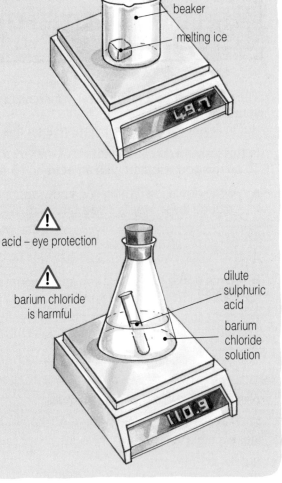

beaker

melting ice

Test 1 – A physical change
- Put a cube of ice in a beaker.
- Quickly put the beaker on the top-pan balance. Measure its mass.
- Leave the beaker until the cube has half melted. Measure its mass again.
- When the ice has all melted, measure its mass again.

What do you notice about the mass?

Test 2 – A chemical change
- Half fill a small tube with dilute sulphuric acid. Carefully put it inside a small conical flask.
- Measure out 25 cm³ of barium chloride solution in a measuring cylinder.
- Carefully use a teat pipette to transfer the solution into the flask.
  Do not drop any solution into the test-tube.
- Put a stopper on the flask. ***Do not let any acid spill into the solution***. Measure the mass of the apparatus.
- Now tip the flask very gently so the 2 liquids mix. How do you know there is a reaction? Measure the mass of the apparatus again.

What do you notice about the mass?

⚠️ acid – eye protection

⚠️ barium chloride is harmful

dilute sulphuric acid

barium chloride solution

In a **physical change**, the mass stays the same.
This is because no new substance is made. The substance just changes its form.

$$H_2O(s) \longrightarrow H_2O(l)$$
solid ice   liquid water

In a **chemical change**, the *total* mass stays the same.
This is because the new substances must be made from the substances already there.
The chemical elements are just combining together in different ways.

$$BaCl_2 + H_2SO_4 \longrightarrow BaSO_4 + 2HCl$$

FAIRY
PURE & GENTLE

original perfume

1 Copy and complete:
a) In a .... change, a new substance is made.
b) In a .... change, no new substance is made.
c) In a chemical change, the total mass ....
....
d) In a physical change, the mass ....
....

2 Melting is a physical change.
a) Describe what happens to the particles as a solid melts.
b) Describe what happens to the particles as a liquid boils.
c) Use your answers to a) and b) to explain why the mass stays the same in a physical change.

3 Which of these are chemical changes?
a) Making soap from vegetable oil.
b) Boiling some water.
c) Burning natural gas.
d) Making aluminium cans from aluminium metal.
e) Making coffee by adding water to coffee powder.
f) Making glass from sand.
g) Baking clay.

4 When hydrogen burns in oxygen, water is made.
$$2H_2 + O_2 \longrightarrow 2H_2O$$
The mass stays the same.
Use the equation to explain why.

Things to do

88 + ●● → (diagram)

Making salts

The word **salt** probably makes you think of something you put on your chips!
But in science a **salt** is much more than this.

In this lesson you can make lots of **different** salts.
To do this you will start with an **acid** and a **metal**.

a Write down everything you know about acids.
Include these words if you can.

| pH | alkali | strong | red | weak | neutral |

b Write down everything you know about metals.
Include these words if you can.

| shiny | conductor | strong | electricity | heat | hard |

Reacting acids with metals

Try these tests with hydrochloric acid and metals.
Make a table to record your results.

Put 5 test-tubes in a rack.
Put about 2 cm³ of dilute hydrochloric acid in each test-tube.
Clean the metal samples with sand paper.
Add the metal samples to the acid as shown.

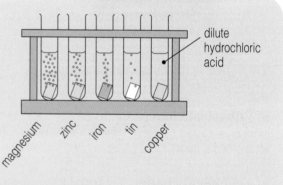

dilute hydrochloric acid

magnesium   zinc   iron   tin   copper

c How do you know if there is a reaction?

d What is the name of the gas given off?

e How can you test for this gas?

If the metal does not react, put the tube in a beaker of hot water.
See if the metal reacts with **warm** acid.

f You could use dilute sulphuric acid now instead of dilute hydrochloric acid.
What do you think would happen?
Ask your teacher if you can check your idea.

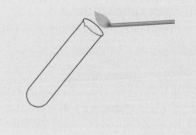

g What do you think would happen with dilute nitric acid and metals?

When a metal reacts with an acid a **salt** is made.

magnesium + hydrochloric acid $\longrightarrow$ ***magnesium chloride*** + hydrogen
$\quad$ Mg $\quad$ + $\quad$ 2HCl $\quad\longrightarrow\quad$ $MgCl_2$ $\quad$ + $\quad$ H_2

magnesium + sulphuric acid $\longrightarrow$ ***magnesium sulphate*** + hydrogen
$\quad$ Mg $\quad$ + $\quad$ H_2SO_4 $\quad\longrightarrow\quad$ $MgSO_4$ $\quad$ + $\quad$ H_2

magnesium + nitric acid $\longrightarrow$ ***magnesium nitrate*** + hydrogen
$\quad$ Mg $\quad$ + $\quad$ 2HNO$_3$ $\quad\longrightarrow\quad$ $Mg(NO_3)_2$ $\quad$ + $\quad$ H_2

sulphuric acid is H_2SO_4
hydrochloric acid is HCl
nitric acid is HNO_3

Salts made from **sulphuric acid** are **sulphates**.
Salts made from **hydrochloric acid** are **chlorides**.
Salts made from **nitric acid** are **nitrates**.

Making zinc sulphate

An acid can be changed to make a salt. The change is a *chemical reaction.*

acid – eye protection

Carry out this experiment to make crystals of a salt. You can use the Help Sheet.

Add zinc powder to dilute sulphuric acid and stir.

When no more zinc dissolves, filter the mixture.

Carefully evaporate the filtrate to half its original volume.
Then leave it to cool.

eye protection

sulphuric acid	+	zinc	⟶	zinc sulphate	+	hydrogen
(**acid**)		(**metal**)		(**salt**)		

Acids are corrosive

h Look at the photographs. Which one shows the hydrogen being made?

i Why should you keep adding zinc until *no more dissolves*?

j What do you see when you evaporate and then cool the solution?

k What is the name of the solid made? This is the product.

l Try to write a symbol equation for the reaction.

Things to do

1 Copy and complete:
a) Acids have pH number . . . . than 7.
b) Acids react with metals to make . . . . and hydrogen.
c) acid + ... ⟶ salt + ...
d) Hydrogen gas . . . . with a . . . . spill.
e) Sulphates are made from . . . . acid.
f) Chlorides are made from . . . . acid.
g) Nitrates are made from . . . . acid.
h) To make zinc chloride we use . . . . and . . . . acid.

2 Acid and metal reactions are used to make lots of salts.
a) Why can't we make copper sulphate this way?
b) Why can't we make sodium sulphate this way?

3 Some solutions were tested with pH paper:

solution	A	B	C	D	E
pH value	9	1	5	13	7

a) Say whether each solution is acidic, alkaline or neutral.

| 1 | 2 | 3 | 4 | 5 | 6 | 7 | 8 | 9 | 10 | 11 | 12 | 13 | 14 |

b) What colour does the pH paper turn with i) D? ii) E? iii) B?
c) Which solution is the most acidic?
d) Which solution could be pure water?

4 Acid rain causes problems. Think about the reactions of acids.
a) What happens when acid rain falls on metal?
b) Limestone is calcium carbonate. What happens when acid rain falls on limestone rock?

31c Acids and bases

We can make a **salt** by reacting acid with metal.

▶ Copy and complete these word equations:

a zinc + nitric acid ⟶

b iron + hydrochloric acid ⟶

c magnesium + sulphuric acid ⟶

Take care with the next one!

d copper + hydrochloric acid ⟶

There are other ways to make salts.
We can react acids with **bases**.
Bases are the oxides, hydroxides and carbonates of metals.

▶ Name the bases with these formulae:

e MgO   **f** $CuCO_3$ **g** $Ca(OH)_2$

The base **neutralises** the acid.

acid	+	**base**	⟶	**salt**	+ **water**
sulphuric	+	magnesium	⟶	magnesium	+ water
acid		oxide		sulphate	
H_2SO_4	+	MgO	⟶	$MgSO_4$	+ H_2O

If the base is the metal **carbonate**, we get another product.

Look at the reaction of magnesium carbonate with acid:

h What causes the fizzing in the reaction?

i How can you test for this gas?

sulphuric	+	magnesium	⟶	magnesium	+	carbon	+	water
acid		carbonate		sulphate		dioxide		
H_2SO_4	+	$MgCO_3$	⟶	$MgSO_4$	+	CO_2	+	H_2O

j Which elements are found in all carbonates?

Your teacher may let you try some other 'carbonate + acid' reactions.
We can use this reaction to prepare carbon dioxide in the laboratory.

Try matching your products to these formulae $FeCl_2$ $MgSO_4$ $Zn(NO_3)_2$

Some common bases

Adding a carbonate to acid

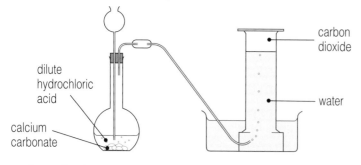

dilute hydrochloric acid

calcium carbonate

carbon dioxide

water

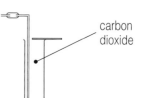

carbon dioxide

The carbon dioxide can be collected **over water**. It is only slightly soluble in water.
We can collect it by **downward delivery**. The gas is denser than air.
It is colourless, so it is difficult to tell when the gas jar is full.

These are the general word equations for acid + base reactions:

acid + **metal oxide** ⟶ **salt** + **water**

acid + **metal hydroxide** ⟶ **salt** + **water**

acid + **metal carbonate** ⟶ **salt** + **carbon dioxide** + **water**

Try using an acid + base reaction to make a salt. You can use the Help Sheet.

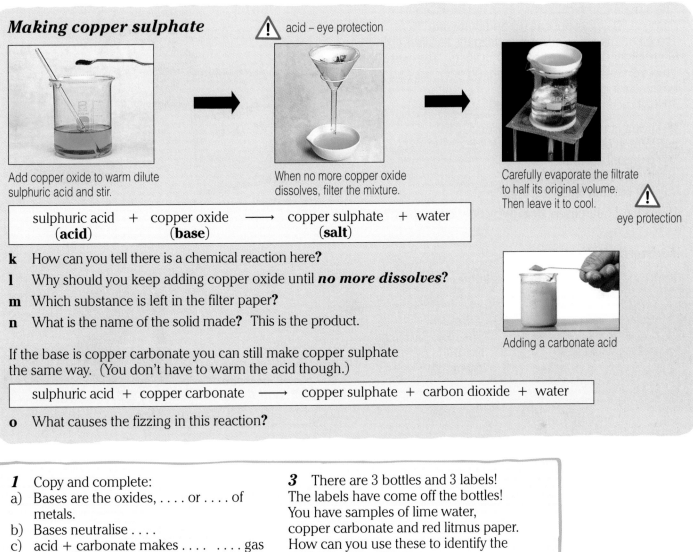

Making copper sulphate

⚠ acid – eye protection

Add copper oxide to warm dilute sulphuric acid and stir.

When no more copper oxide dissolves, filter the mixture.

Carefully evaporate the filtrate to half its original volume. Then leave it to cool.

⚠ eye protection

sulphuric acid	+	copper oxide	⟶	copper sulphate	+ water
(**acid**)		(**base**)		(**salt**)	

k How can you tell there is a chemical reaction here?

l Why should you keep adding copper oxide until *no more dissolves*?

m Which substance is left in the filter paper?

n What is the name of the solid made? This is the product.

Adding a carbonate acid

If the base is copper carbonate you can still make copper sulphate the same way. (You don't have to warm the acid though.)

sulphuric acid + copper carbonate ⟶ copper sulphate + carbon dioxide + water

o What causes the fizzing in this reaction?

---

1 Copy and complete:
a) Bases are the oxides, ... or . . . . of metals.
b) Bases neutralise . . . .
c) acid + carbonate makes . . . . gas
d) . . . . + metal oxide makes a salt.

2 You have 5 test-tubes containing different gases. The gases are:

nitrogen	oxygen	carbon dioxide
	hydrogen	air

How can you identify each gas?
Describe the tests and the results.

This gas puts out a burning splint.

That doesn't *prove* it's carbon dioxide.

3 There are 3 bottles and 3 labels!
The labels have come off the bottles!
You have samples of lime water, copper carbonate and red litmus paper.
How can you use these to identify the liquid in the bottles?
Describe what you would do.

DISTILLED WATER   SULPHURIC ACID   SODIUM HYDROXIDE

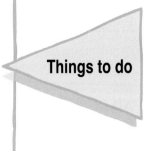

Things to do

Salt of the Earth

Some salts can be used as fertilisers.
The 3 main chemical elements in fertilisers are:
nitrogen (N), phosphorus (P) and potassium (K).
The elements are in **compounds** in the fertiliser.
On fertiliser bags you often see numbers. These are **NPK** ratios.
They tell you how much nitrogen, phosphorus and potassium
the fertiliser contains.
16.8.24 means 16%N, 8%P, 24%K.

▶ Look at these bags of fertilisers:
a Which of these fertilisers:
  i) contain nitrogen?
  ii) contain phosphorus?
  iii) contain all 3 elements?

b What do fertilisers do? Why do we use them?

Using fertilisers

Rupa and Tim are talking about fertilisers.

I think it's best to put the fertiliser in the soil before you plant the seeds.

No. You should plant the seeds first and then add the fertiliser.

Who do you think is right?
Plan an investigation to find out.
In the next activity you can make a fertiliser.
You can use it to carry out your investigation.

Making a fertiliser

You can make a simple fertiliser called ammonium sulphate
in the lab.

Ammonium sulphate has the formula $(NH_4)_2SO_4$
c Which chemical elements does it contain?

Ammonium sulphate is a salt. It is made by neutralising an acid.
Alkalis neutralise acids.
An **alkali** is a special kind of base – it dissolves in water.

The reaction to make a fertiliser is a **neutralisation**.

| acid + alkali ⟶ salt + water |
| (base) |

Sodium hydroxide is a base. It is also an alkali.

Copper oxide is a base. It is **not** an alkali.

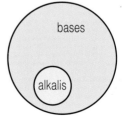

bases

alkalis

192

Making ammonium sulphate

⚠ acid – eye protection

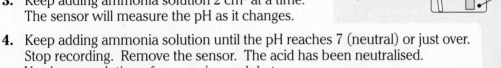

stand
burette
ammonia solution
plastic stirring rod
interface
pH sensor
20 cm³ dilute sulphuric acid

1. Put 20 cm³ of dilute sulphuric acid into a beaker. Put a pH sensor into the acid. Note the pH reading. Start recording.

2. Fill a burette with ammonia solution. Add 2 cm³ of ammonia solution to the acid. Stir very carefully with a plastic stirrer. Be careful not to touch the sensor with the stirrer.

3. Keep adding ammonia solution 2 cm³ at a time. The sensor will measure the pH as it changes.

4. Keep adding ammonia solution until the pH reaches 7 (neutral) or just over. Stop recording. Remove the sensor. The acid has been neutralised. You have a solution of ammonium sulphate.

sulphuric acid	**+**	**ammonia solution**	⟶	**ammonium sulphate**	**+ water**
(acid)		(alkali)		(salt)	
H_2SO_4	+	$2NH_4OH$	⟶	$(NH_4)_2SO_4$	+ $2H_2O$

5.

HEAT ⚠ hot

Pour the solution into an evaporating basin. Carefully evaporate the water from the solution by heating it on a water bath. Evaporate until only half of the original solution is left.

6. Leave the basin to cool. Crystals of ammonium sulphate will form slowly. Filter the crystals from any solution left. Dry them between filter papers.

What does your fertiliser look like?
You can use this fertiliser to carry out your investigation (page 192).

---

1 Copy and complete:
a) 3 common elements in fertilisers are . . . . , ... and . . . .
b) NP fertilisers contain . . . . and . . . .
c) An . . . . is a base that dissolves in water.
d) Ammonium sulphate is made from dilute . . . . acid.

2 Look at these NPK values for 4 fertilisers:

0.24.24	15.15.21	25.0.16	27.5.5
1	**2**	**3**	**4**

a) Which fertiliser contains most nitrogen?
b) Which fertiliser contains least nitrogen?
c) Which one is NK fertiliser?
d) Which fertiliser contains the same % of nitrogen as phosphorus?
e) Fertilisers can cause water pollution. Explain why.
f) Plants also need small amounts of: Ca Mg Na Cu Zn S Fe Name these elements.

3 Visit a garden centre. Look at packets of fertilisers recommended for growing
i) fruit (e.g. tomatoes)
ii) grass
iii) flowers
a) Make a list of NPK values for these fertilisers.
b) Can you draw any conclusions about the elements needed to grow certain crops?

4 What are *organic vegetables*? Why do some people want to buy these even if they are more expensive?

Things to do

What's the use?

Some reactions are useful. Others, like rusting, are not useful.

▶ What makes a reaction useful? Write down your ideas.
Look at the photos opposite:
They all show the results of a chemical reaction.
Say whether you think the reaction is **useful** or **not useful**.
Explain why.

Neutralisation

acid + base ⟶ salt + water

This is a **neutralisation**.
You know that neutralisation can be a useful reaction.
Fertiliser can be made this way.
Other acid + base reactions are useful too.

a

b

c

d

e

f What does 'milk of magnesia' do?
g How is toothpaste used in a neutralisation?
h Why can you treat a wasp sting with vinegar?

Making quicklime

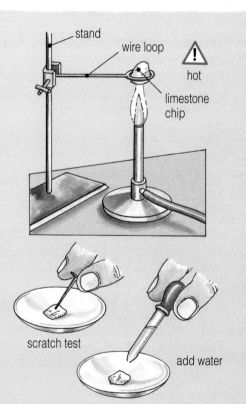

stand
wire loop
hot
limestone chip

scratch test

add water

Here's a chance for *you* to carry out a useful reaction.

Take 2 limestone chips which look similar.
Heat one chip strongly in a hot Bunsen flame.
Heat it for 10 minutes. Then let the chip cool.
Compare the heated and unheated chips:
- Appearance – what do they look like?
- Do they scratch easily? Use an iron nail to test.
  (Don't touch the solids.)
- Add 2 drops of water to each chip and test with pH paper.
- Add one drop of dilute acid to each.

Record all your results in a table.
Do you notice any difference between the chips?

acid

When you heated the limestone chip it decomposed (broke down).
Two products were made in the reaction:

calcium carbonate	⟶	calcium oxide	+	carbon dioxide
limestone		quicklime		
$CaCO_3$	⟶	CaO	+	CO_2

i What happened to the carbon dioxide?
j Quicklime is an alkali. Sometimes farmers use it on soil. Why?

Burning fuels

Your teacher may show you this experiment:

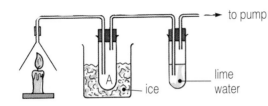

You can burn fuels containing carbon and hydrogen.

k What do you see in tube A?

l How can you test if this is water?

m What happens to the lime water?

If there is enough oxygen, the fuel makes carbon dioxide (CO_2). This is a **combustion** reaction.

If there is not enough oxygen the combustion is *incomplete*. This means carbon monoxide (CO) is also made. Some carbon (C) itself may be given off too. This is soot. It makes the flame look smoky.

Can burning be a useful reaction?

Car exhaust fumes contain carbon monoxide.

Global warming

Global warming is caused by the **greenhouse effect**.

Carbon dioxide is a 'greenhouse gas'. It is important because it traps heat that would otherwise escape into space. It keeps the Earth warm for us. But we are disturbing the natural balance of carbon dioxide in the atmosphere. We are making so much of it that the Earth is warming up very quickly.

n How are we making so much carbon dioxide?

o What will be the effects if global warming continues?

p What could we do to reduce global warming?

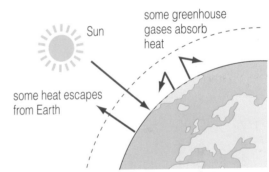

Carbon dioxide and water vapour are 'greenhouse gases'.

Things to do

1 Copy out each description of a reaction. Which reaction best fits the description? Match the reaction to its description.

Description	Reaction
• A useful reaction which can make some nasty products.	• Fermenting sugar
• A slow reaction which is not useful.	• Burning a fuel
• A slow reaction which makes alcohol.	• Rusting of iron

2 Carbon dioxide and water vapour are 'greenhouse gases'. Find out the names and formulae of some other greenhouse gases.

3 Find out about these fuels:

> wood   ethanol   hydrogen

Make a list of the advantages and disadvantages of each one.

4 Ethene has the formula C_2H_4. It can be made from crude oil.
a) Find out about useful products from reactions of ethene.
b) Ethene burns in air. What will the products be?

31f Finding the energy

Do you enjoy November 5th?
Bonfire night is about chemical reactions!

▶ The chemical reactions in fireworks transfer energy.
Write about all the energy transfers in the photo.

Most chemical reactions **give out** energy.
They are called **exothermic** reactions.
But some reactions **take in** energy from the surroundings.
These are called **endothermic** reactions.

Your mouth feels cold when you eat sherbet.
The reaction of sherbet with water is **endothermic**.
The reaction takes in heat energy from your mouth so it cools it
down.

Energy in or out?

Try some of these reactions. See what happens to the temperature.

1. Dissolve some citric acid in 50 cm³ water.
   Note the temperature of the solution.

   Add crushed limestone to the solution, one spatula measure
   at a time. Stir and note the temperature after each addition.
   Add 5 spatula measures in total.

   What do you notice?
   Is this an exothermic or endothermic reaction?

2. Repeat experiment 1 but add sodium bicarbonate (sodium
   hydrogencarbonate) instead of crushed limestone.
   What do you notice?
   Is this an exothermic or endothermic reaction?

3. Measure 25 cm³ of dilute sulphuric acid into a beaker.
   Note the temperature of the solution.

   Add 5 cm³ of sodium hydroxide solution to the acid. Stir and
   note the temperature of the solution. Repeat this until 30 cm³
   of sodium hydroxide have been added.
   What do you notice?
   Is this an exothermic or endothermic reaction?

4. Light a Bunsen burner.
   Natural gas burns.

   What do you notice?
   Is this an exothermic or endothermic reaction?

Do **not** measure
the temperature of
the flame. Just observe.

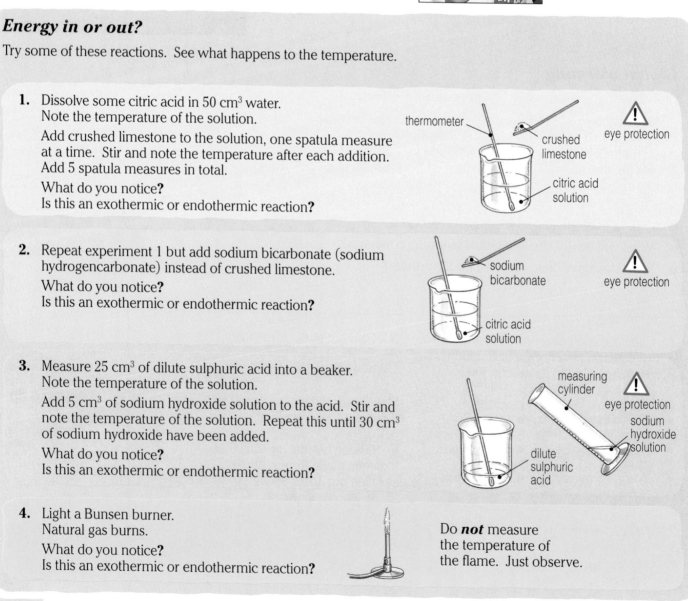

Lab in chaos

eye protection

Five glass bottles are in the lab.
They all contain colourless liquids.
Four have lost their labels. One is labelled *dilute sulphuric acid*.

You have only 2 beakers and one thermometer.
How can you find out which of the 4 solutions are alkalis?
Write a plan for your teacher.
Have your plan checked. Then do it!

Energy is always transferred when a chemical change takes place.
Sometimes we can observe this
- the temperature may change
- we may see light or hear sound.

Think about these energy changes from
chemical reactions.

You may have seen these in
camping shops.
They keep your hands warm for
several hours.

a How do you think they work?

Have you ever bought one of these?
They are popular at outdoor concerts.

b How do you think they work?

c Why is this so useful?

But sometimes the energy transfer can be a problem.
Look at the newspaper extract.

d What should you do if you smell a gas leak?

Explosion wrecks home!

Workmen who picked their way through the rubble of a house demolished by a gas explosion yesterday found 94-year-old Mrs Ivy Shepherd still standing in the kitchen where she had been eating a cheese sandwich.

The roof and timbers had collapsed around Mrs Shepherd, a widow, but she was unharmed and her only complaint was of the dust in her white hair and a torn apron.

She was taken to hospital in Worthing, West Sussex, for a check-up but was later released.

Things to do

1 Copy and complete:
a) Chemical reactions which give out energy are called . . . .
b) Chemical reactions which take in energy are called . . . .
c) In an . . . . reaction the temperature of the reaction mixture rises.
d) In an . . . . reaction the temperature of the reaction mixture falls.
e) Burning a fuel in air is an . . . . reaction.
f) Neutralisation is an . . . . reaction.
g) Dissolving sherbet in water is an . . . . reaction.

2 Spirit burners can be used to burn liquid fuels safely in the lab.
Plan an investigation to compare the amount of energy transferred when different fuels are burnt.

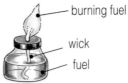

burning fuel
wick
fuel

3 Is respiration an exothermic or endothermic reaction?
How do you know?

31g What's your reaction?

You have already met lots of chemical reactions.

▶ Remind yourself of some reactions. Copy and complete these word equations:

a iron + oxygen ⟶ . . . . (rust)

b acid + metal ⟶ . . . . + ...

c acid + carbonate ⟶ salt + ... + ...

d acid + base ⟶ . . . . + water

e fuel + oxygen ⟶ . . . . + ... + energy

Do you remember about **displacement** reactions?

▶ Rosie tested 4 metals to see which would react with solutions of metal sulphates.
Use the reactivity series to predict her results.
Use a copy of the table. Put a tick (✓) if the metal reacts.
Put a cross (✗) if the metal does not react.

zinc	iron	magnesium	copper	
			✗	copper sulphate
		✗		magnesium sulphate
	✗			iron sulphate
✗				zinc sulphate

Reactivity series
potassium
magnesium
zinc
iron
tin
copper

Displacement reactions and energy

Compare the energy changes when different metals are added to copper sulphate solution.
Plan your investigation.
● How will you make your tests fair?
● How will you measure the energy changes?
Have your plan checked by your teacher. Then carry it out.

Look closely at your results. Look at the reactivity series.
Do you notice a pattern?

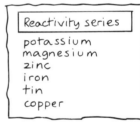

Don't throw that away. I need it to fill up the car.

The future

What about the future? New chemical reactions will make new materials.

. . . making petrol from paper?
It is possible to make oil from waste paper. At the moment the oil is just suitable for boiler fuel. But in the future it may be possible to change this to petrol and plastic.

. . . hydrogen to fuel a car?
The hydrogen reacts with oxygen to drive the engine.

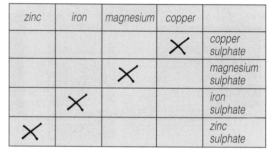

. . . a cure for flu?
Scientists are using computers to help them design a molecule which may cure flu.

A best seller

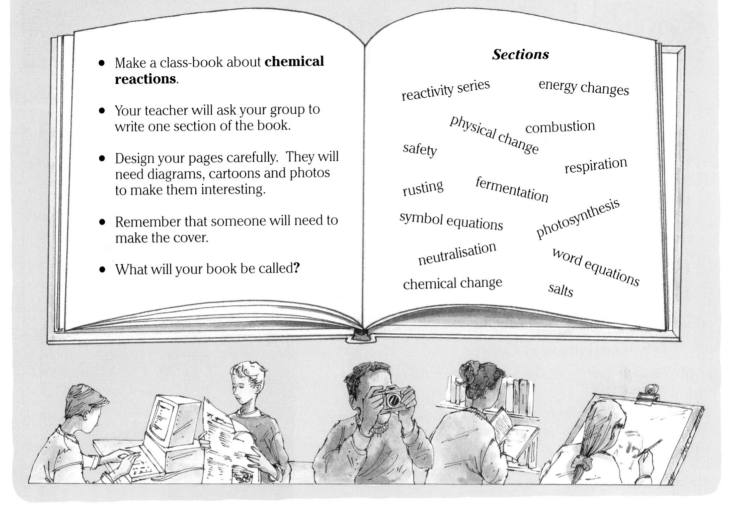

- Make a class-book about **chemical reactions**.

- Your teacher will ask your group to write one section of the book.

- Design your pages carefully. They will need diagrams, cartoons and photos to make them interesting.

- Remember that someone will need to make the cover.

- What will your book be called?

Sections

reactivity series   energy changes

physical change   combustion

safety

respiration

rusting   fermentation

symbol equations   photosynthesis

neutralisation   word equations

chemical change   salts

Things to do

1 Copy and complete using a word from the box:

> hydrogen   oxygen   combustion
> neutralisation   fermentation

a) . . . . is a reaction in which a fuel burns in air.
b) Reacting acid and metal makes . . . .
c) . . . . is the making of alcohol from sugar.
d) Respiration uses . . . . gas.
e) The reaction between an acid and a base is . . . .

2 Chemical reactions don't always happen. Think about the reactivity series. Predict whether a reaction will take place in each case.
a) magnesium + iron oxide
b) zinc oxide + copper
c) copper sulphate + zinc
d) magnesium sulphate + copper

3 Link the raw material in the list with the made material on the right, e.g. sand is used to make glass.

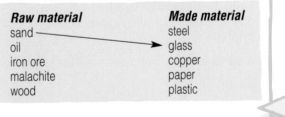

Raw material	Made material
sand	steel
oil	glass
iron ore	copper
malachite	paper
wood	plastic

4 Use books and ROMs to find out how some of these things are made.
a) soap
b) bread
c) polythene
d) glass
e) yoghurt.

Chemistry at Work

31h

Combustion

Rockets escaping the gravitational pull of the Earth need fuels that burn very fiercely.
Liquid hydrogen and liquid oxygen are used.
It was a leak in the fuel tanks that caused the space shuttle disaster in 1986.

a Write a word equation for hydrogen reacting with oxygen.

Hydrogen is sometimes called the fuel of the future.

b Why are we searching for fuels to take the place of petrol and diesel?

c Which common compound could be a useful source of hydrogen in the future?

d Find out how we can get hydrogen from the compound in question **c**.

e Explain why burning hydrogen will be better for our environment than burning petrol.

f Write about some of the problems that we will have to overcome if we do ever use hydrogen as a major fuel in the future.

Neutralisation

You know that an acid and an alkali react together.
You might have used one of these neutralisation reactions to make ammonium sulphate.

g Name the acid and alkali used to make ammonium sulphate.

h Is ammonium sulphate:
  i) a metal?
  ii) a non-metal?
  iii) a salt?
  iv) an alkali?

The chemical formula of ammonium sulphate is $(NH_4)_2SO_4$.

i Which important element does ammonium sulphate provide for plants?

What are the NPK values for ammonium sulphate?

Another important fertiliser is ammonium nitrate.
Its formula is NH_4NO_3.

j How many different elements are there in ammonium nitrate?

k How many atoms are shown in the formula of nitric acid, HNO_3?

l Write a brief method you could use to make ammonium nitrate in the lab. You must bear in mind that ammonium nitrate can explode if you heat the solid too strongly.

In industry the reaction is carried out as shown below:

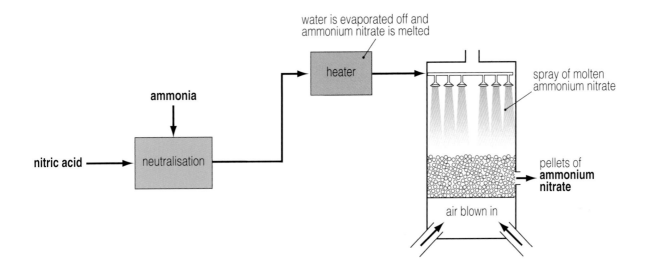

water is evaporated off and
ammonium nitrate is melted

heater

ammonia

spray of molten
ammonium nitrate

nitric acid → neutralisation

pellets of
**ammonium
nitrate**

air blown in

m Find out the chemical formula of ammonia.

n Find out the chemical formula of nitric acid.

o Write a word equation for making ammonium nitrate.

p Find out all the raw materials you would need to make ammonia and nitric acid in industry.

q Describe the ideal site to put a fertiliser factory that manufactures ammonium nitrate.
Think about the raw materials you will need and anything else you feel is important.
Explain all your reasoning.

r Why is the plant in the photograph situated well away from any houses?

s Write a letter to your local council which has just given planning permission for a fertiliser factory next to your school.

t Find out about the pollution that fertilisers like ammonium nitrate can cause.

Questions

1 Which of these are physical changes?
a) Adding water to orange squash.
b) Burning petrol in a car engine.
c) Getting salt from sea water.
d) Making detergent from crude oil.

2 Gavin heated some magnesium ribbon in air.
He measured the mass of solid before and after heating.
Here are his results:
Mass of solid before heating = 0.24 g
Mass of solid after heating = 0.40 g
a) Copy and complete the word equation for the reaction:
   magnesium + ... $\longrightarrow$ magnesium oxide
b) Name the solid product of the reaction.
c) Try to explain Gavin's results.

3 Explain how you could make a sample of solid magnesium sulphate
starting with magnesium ribbon and dilute sulphuric acid.
Write a method. Draw diagrams.

4 You have used lots of chemicals to carry out reactions.
Some chemicals are dangerous. They must be used very carefully.
They have hazard labels on their containers.
Look at the hazard labels opposite. Draw sketches of them.
Explain what each hazard label tells us.

5 Name the products of these reactions:
a) iron + sulphuric acid
b) zinc carbonate + sulphuric acid
c) magnesium oxide + nitric acid
d) sodium hydroxide + hydrochloric acid

6 Stomach powders help to neutralise acids in your stomach.
Plan an investigation to find out which stomach powder is the
best value for money.

7 Handwarmers are okay, but . . . .
Invent some self-warming soup for winter walks.
a) Design a can of soup which can warm itself when opened.
b) Make an advertisement for your invention.

8 Can scientists help to solve some of the world's problems?
Imagine **you** could make some new materials to solve these
problems.
What would you want your new materials to do?
Make a list of your ideas.

Electricity and Magnetism

32

Electricity is important to all of us.
Our lives would be very different without it.

We use electricity to transfer energy from one place to another.
We use it for lighting and for heating.

And we can use electricity to make magnets – which we use
every day in radios, TVs, and many other things.

In series

▶ The diagram shows a circuit with 2 bulbs in **series**:

a What does each symbol stand for?

b What can you say about the current through **A** and the current through **B**?

c What happens if bulb **B** breaks? Why?

d Draw a circuit diagram of 3 bulbs in series.

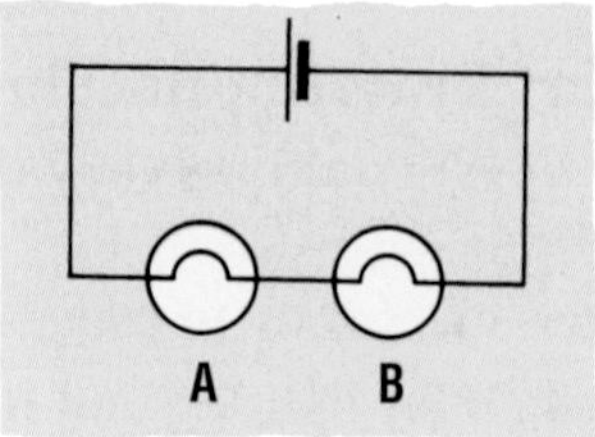

Bulbs in series

Energy from a battery

A battery pushes electrons (−) round the circuit:

The flow of electrons is called a **current**. The size of the current is measured in amperes (amps, A).

e What meter would you use to measure the current?

The electrons transfer energy from the cell to the bulbs. The higher the **voltage** of the battery, the more energy the electrons can transfer:

f What meter would you use to measure the voltage?

The energy transferred by the electrons is used to heat up the filament. Some of this heat energy is transformed to light energy, which is then transferred by radiation.

g Draw an Energy Transfer Diagram for this circuit.

A conductor lets electrons pass through it easily. It has a low **resistance**.
An insulator has a high resistance. The electrons cannot move through the insulator, so there is no current.

h Write down the names of 3 conductors and 3 insulators.

i 'Mains' voltage is 230 V. Why is this dangerous?

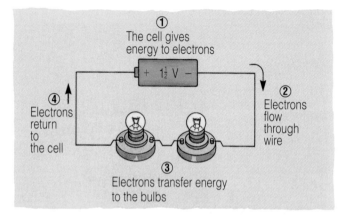

① The cell gives energy to electrons

+ 1½ V −

④ Electrons return to the cell

② Electrons flow through wire

③ Electrons transfer energy to the bulbs

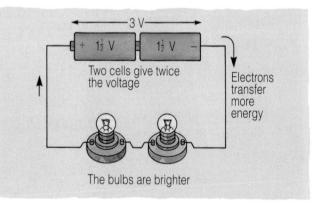

←—— 3 V ——→

+ 1½ V   1½ V −

Two cells give twice the voltage

Electrons transfer more energy

The bulbs are brighter

▶ Here are some of the symbols used in circuit diagrams.

j Copy the symbols and label each one.

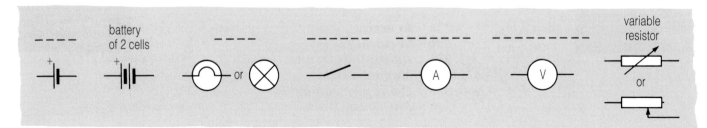

battery of 2 cells

variable resistor

or

A   V

or

Reading ammeters

The diagrams show two ammeters:

What are the readings **k**, **l**, **m**, **n**, **o**, and **p?**

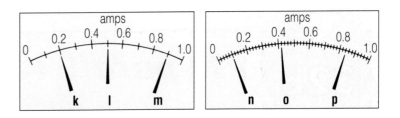

Measuring currents

Here is a series circuit:

- Draw a circuit diagram for it.

- Then connect up the circuit. Make sure the + terminal of the ammeter is connected to the + terminal of the battery.

- Adjust the variable resistor to make the bulb as bright as possible.
  What is the reading on the ammeter?

- Disconnect the ammeter and then re-connect it in position 2.
  What is the reading now?
  What is the reading on the ammeter if it is in position 3?
  Write a sentence to describe what you found.

- Now connect a second bulb in **series**.
  What happens to the brightness of the first bulb?
  What happens to the current through the ammeter?
  Explain why you think this happens, using the words:
  current   **electrons**   **resistance**

- Predict what would happen if you added a third bulb in series. Try it if you can.

- With just one bulb, use the variable resistor to reduce the current until the bulb is not quite glowing.
  What is the reading on your ammeter now?

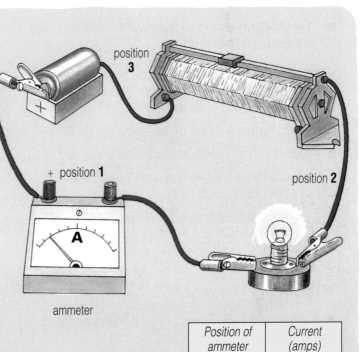

ammeter

Position of ammeter	Current (amps)
1	
2	
3	

A digital ammeter

---

1 Copy and complete:
In a **series** circuit,
a) The current is the . . . . through each part of the circuit. It is not used up.
b) If you add extra bulbs, the current is . . . . and the bulbs are . . . . bright.
c) If you add extra cells, the electrons have . . . . energy and bulbs shine . . . . brightly.
d) An ammeter measures the . . . . in a circuit, in . . . . or A.
e) A battery pushes . . . . round a circuit. The size of the push is measured in . . . . , by using a . . . .
f) A good conductor has a . . . . resistance.

2 An ammeter is connected in series with a battery, a switch and a bulb.
a) Draw the circuit diagram.
b) If the ammeter reads 0.8 A, how much current passes through the bulb?
c) A second bulb is connected in series. Draw the circuit diagram.
d) The ammeter reading is now 0.4 A. How much current passes through each bulb now?
e) Explain why this current is less than before.

3 The ampere and the volt are named after André Ampère and Alessandro Volta. Find out more about these people and what they did.

Things to do

In parallel

▶ The diagram shows a circuit with 2 bulbs connected in **parallel**:

When the electrons travel from the battery, **some** of them go through bulb **A**, and the rest of them go through bulb **B**.

a What happens if one of the bulbs breaks?

b Draw a circuit diagram of 3 bulbs in parallel.

c Now re-draw your circuit with 3 switches, one to control each bulb.

d Then add a fourth switch to switch off all the bulbs together.

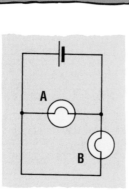

Bulbs in parallel

Measuring currents

• Connect up this circuit, with the **ammeter** in position 1:
  Take care to connect the ammeter correctly.

• What is the reading on your ammeter?

• Then connect the ammeter in position 2.
  What is the current through bulb **A**?

• Then find the current in position 3.

• What do you notice about your results?
  Explain this, using these words:
  current   electrons   resistance

Notice the ammeter is always in series in the circuit.

Calculating currents

Look carefully at this circuit:

Suppose you are told the readings on 3 of the ammeters are:
$A_2 = 1 A$ $A_3 = 1 A$ $A_4 = 1.5 A$

e What is the reading on ammeter A_5?

f What is the reading on ammeter A_6?

g What is the reading on ammeter A_1?

h If more cells are put in the circuit to increase the voltage, what would you expect to happen to each of the ammeter readings?

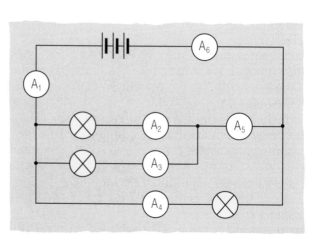

Measuring voltages – 1

Connect up this circuit with a cell and 2 bulbs in parallel:

A **voltmeter** is connected *in parallel* with the bulbs.

Use your voltmeter to measure:
- the voltage across bulb **1** (V_1),
- the voltage across bulb **2** (V_2),
- the voltage across the cell (V_3).

What do you find?

Can you explain this?

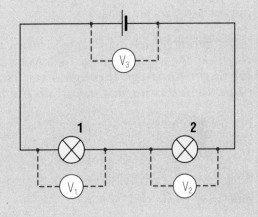
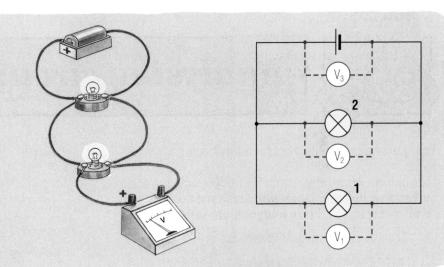

Measuring voltages – 2

Now connect 2 bulbs in series with a cell as shown:

Use your voltmeter to measure:
- the voltage across bulb **1** (V_1),
- the voltage across bulb **2** (V_2),
- the voltage across the cell (V_3).

What do you notice about your results?

Try a third bulb in series. What do you find now?

Notice that the bulbs are in series but the voltmeter is **always in parallel** with a component.

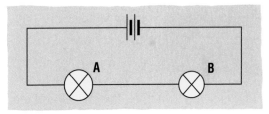

Calculating voltages

In this circuit, a voltmeter connected across the cell reads 3 V. A voltmeter placed across bulb **A** reads 2 V.

i What is the voltage across bulb **B**?

j Which bulb do you think gets more energy? Why?

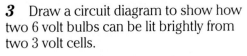

---

1 Copy and complete:
a) An ammeter measures the . . . . passing through a component, so it is always put in . . . . with the component.
b) A voltmeter measures the . . . . across a component, so it is always put in . . . . , across the component.

2 Here is a circuit with 3 ammeters:

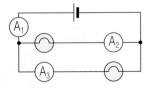

If ammeter A_1 shows 0.5 A and A_2 shows 0.3 A, what is the reading on A_3?

3 Draw a circuit diagram to show how two 6 volt bulbs can be lit brightly from two 3 volt cells.

4 Here is a circuit with 4 voltmeters:

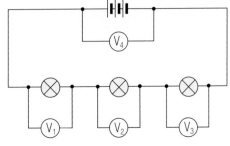

If voltmeters V_1, V_2, V_3 all show 2 V, what is the reading on V_4?

Things to do

Analysing circuits

a Draw a circuit diagram for a torch.

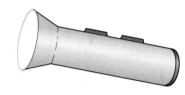

Rashid invents a safety torch for people walking at night.
It has a white bulb at the front and a red bulb at the rear,
with switches to control each of them separately.

b Draw a circuit diagram for him.

Luke suggests this circuit for Rashid's torch:

c Will it work?

d Can you see a disadvantage?

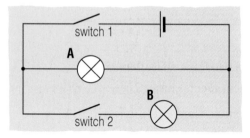

To analyse the circuit, use your finger to follow the path of the
electrons from the cell through the bulb A and back to the cell.
*If your finger has to go through a switch,
then this switch is needed to put on the light.*

Use this method to answer these questions:

e Which switches are needed to light the green lamp?

f Which switches are needed to light the red and blue
lamps together?

g What happens if both switches 3 and 7 are closed?

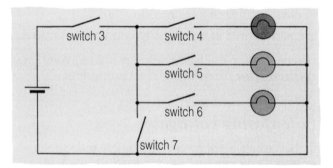

h How can you switch on the buzzer and the lamp?

i What happens if only switches **P** and **R** are closed?

j Re-draw the circuit so that the fan, lamp and buzzer
each have their own switch.

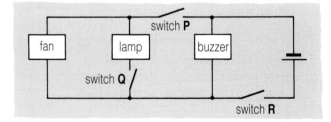

k Draw a circuit with a battery of 2 cells, a switch, an
ammeter, 2 bulbs, and a variable resistor, all in series.
Add a voltmeter in parallel with one of the bulbs.

In this circuit, 2 of the lamps have been **short-circuited**
by a thick wire:

l What happens when the switch is closed?

m Re-draw the circuit so only lamp **Z** is short-circuited.

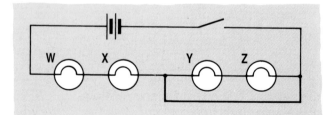

Two-way switches

The diagram shows a switch that can be in position A *or* in position B.

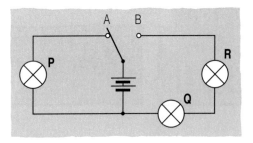

n What happens if the switch is in position A?

o What happens if the switch is in position B?

The diagram shows a mains circuit in a house, with two 2-way switches:
Wire C can be connected to either A or B.
This circuit is often used for the lighting on a staircase.

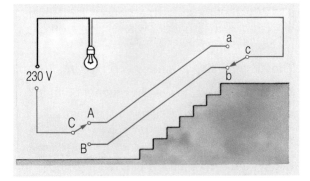

p In the diagram, is the lamp on or off?

q Describe how the circuit works, using the letters on the diagram in your answer.

r What are the advantages of this circuit?

Here is the diagram for a motor in a toy crane:

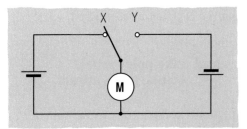

s What do you notice about the cells?

t What happens if the switch is moved from X to Y?

Here is a more complicated circuit:

u Copy and complete this table.

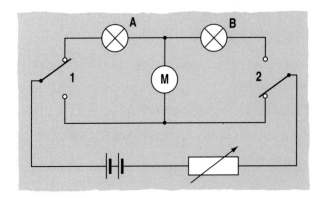

Switch 1	Switch 2	Bulb lit?	Motor turns?
up	down	A	forwards
up	up		
down	up		
down	down		

v What would be the effects of varying the resistor?

Things to do

1 Draw a circuit containing a cell, a switch and 3 bulbs labelled A, B and C. Bulbs A and B are in series, and C is in parallel with A. The switch controls only bulb C.
When all the bulbs are lit, which one is the brightest?

2 Draw a circuit with a 2-way switch, a cell, a bulb, and a motor so that in one position the bulb is on and in the other position the motor is on.

3 In these circuits, all the bulbs are the same:

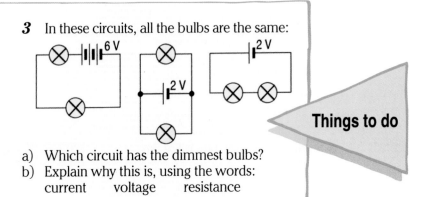

a) Which circuit has the dimmest bulbs?

b) Explain why this is, using the words:
    current   voltage   resistance

Magnetic fields

You can use a magnet to pick up paper-clips, but not paper. Paper is not magnetic.

a Which of these are magnetic: wood, iron, plastic, steel, cloth, a coin, copper wire, nickel, iron oxide**?**

The diagram shows a magnet on a cork, floating on water:

b Which direction will the magnet point to**?**

c What is the name of this instrument**?**

The ends of the bar magnet are called **poles**.

d Which end of a magnet is the N-pole**?**

e If another magnet is brought near, so that its N-pole is near the N-pole of this magnet, what happens**?**

f What happens if a S-pole is brought near a N-pole**?**

a magnet on a floating cork

We say that: **Like poles repel,**
 Unlike poles attract.

The magnets exert a force on each other without touching. This is because a magnet has a **magnetic field** round it. Iron and steel are affected by a magnetic field.

The Earth has a magnetic field round it. This field makes a compass point to the North.

We cannot see a magnetic field, but we can plot a map of it.

Plotting magnetic fields

Put a magnet under a sheet of paper, as shown:

Sprinkle a few iron filings over the paper, and then tap the paper. The iron filings act like tiny compasses.

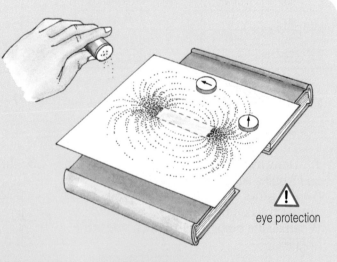

Look carefully at the pattern that appears:

- Sketch the shape of this field.
  The curved lines are called **field lines** or lines of force.

- Use a small 'plotting compass' to follow a field line from the N-pole to the S-pole.

eye protection

Now find the shape of the magnetic field when 2 magnets are placed in line, with

a) The two N-poles near each other like this:
b) A N-pole near a S-pole.

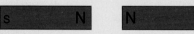

Your teacher can give you a Help Sheet.

Electromagnetism

In 1820, a Danish scientist called Hans Oersted discovered that:
an electric current produces a magnetic field.

In this experiment, a large current is passed up the thick copper wire.
Iron filings are sprinkled on the card to show the shape of the magnetic field:

Plotting compasses show the direction of the field lines.

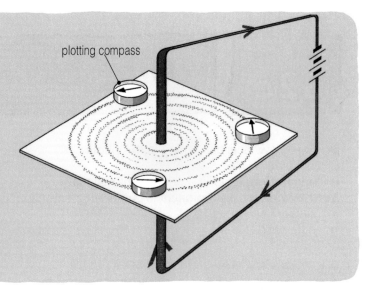

plotting compass

g What happens if the current is reversed?

h What happens to the compasses when the current is switched off?

The magnetic field from a single wire is very weak. To make it stronger, the wire is made into a **coil**, or **solenoid**.

The field round a coil

Iron filings are sprinkled on a card round a coil:

i What happens when the current is switched on?

j What do you notice about the shape of the magnetic field? (Hint: see the opposite page.)

The compasses show the direction of the magnetic field.

k What happens if the current is reversed?

l What happens to the compasses when the current is switched off?

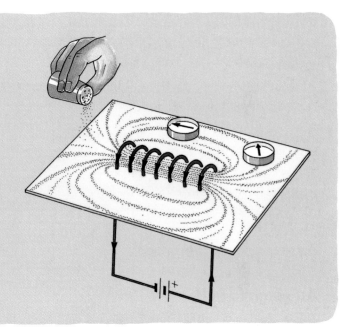

A coil like this is an **electromagnet**.
An electromagnet usually has an iron **core**, which becomes magnetised and makes a stronger electromagnet.

You will use an electromagnet in the next lesson.

---

1 Copy and complete:
a) Like poles .... Unlike poles ....
b) The Earth has a magnetic .... round it.
c) A magnetic .... can be produced by an electric ....
d) The .... field round a straight .... is in the shape of circles.
e) The field round a coil (or ....) has the same shape as the .... round a bar ....
f) An electromagnet only works if a .... is flowing through the ....

2 Drink cans are usually made from either steel or aluminium. In a metal re-cycling plant they need to be separated. Design a machine to do this.

3 In the diagrams below, **A, B, C, D** are compasses. In diagram (a), a current is flowing **down**, into the paper.
In diagram (b), there is no current flowing.
Copy the diagrams and draw in the direction of each compass needle.

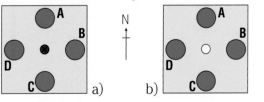

a)   b)

4 Plan an investigation to see if iron can be made into a magnet more easily than steel. How would you make it a fair test?

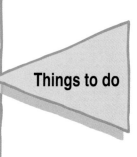

Things to do

Using electromagnets

▶ Explain what is happening in this photo:

Is it an electromagnet or a permanent magnet?
In what ways are electromagnets and permanent magnets
a   similar?
b   different?

Investigating electromagnets

Plan an investigation to find out **what affects the strength of an electromagnet**.

- **What things can you vary?**
  Choose **one** of these, and plan your investigation.

- How will you make it a fair test?

- How will you measure the strength of your electromagnet?

Show your plan to your teacher, and then do it.
Do not use electricity at more than 12 volts!

- If you have time, investigate the other variables.

Electromagnets have many uses.

An electric bell

This is used in doorbells, burglar alarms, and fire-bells.

Study the diagram:

c   When the switch is closed, there is a complete circuit. What happens to the electromagnet?

The iron bar is on a springy metal strip which can bend.

d   What happens to the iron bar?
e   What happens to the hammer?

There is now a gap in the circuit, because the iron bar is not touching the contact.

f   What happens now?

g   Why does the bell ring for as long as the switch is closed?

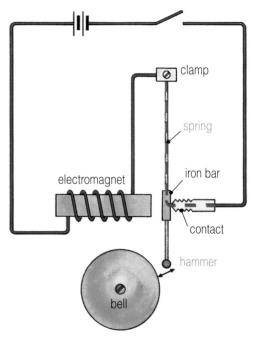

A relay

This is a switch operated by an electromagnet.
It is used when you want to use a small current
to switch on a larger current.

Study the diagram:

There are 2 circuits here.

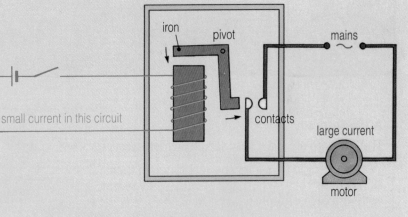

h When a current flows in the blue circuit,
what happens to the core of the coil?

i What happens to the iron bar?

j What happens to the contacts in the
red circuit?

k What happens to the motor?

The motor might be the starter-motor in a car, or
the motor in a washing-machine, or in an electric train.

A circuit-breaker

This is an automatic safety switch.
It cuts off the current if it gets too big.

Study the diagram:

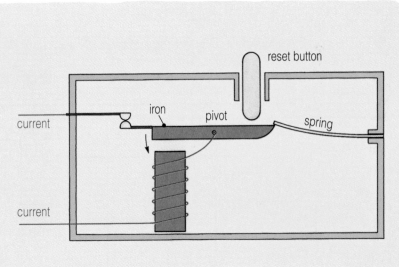

l What happens to the electromagnet when
the current is flowing?

m If the current is big, what happens to
the iron bar?

n What does this do to the current?

o How would you re-set this circuit-breaker?

p To make it switch off at a lower current,
how would you change the electromagnet?

Electromagnets are also used in loudspeakers, in motors, in cassette-recorders,
and in computers to store data on the computer discs.

---

1 Copy and complete:
The strength of an electromagnet can be
increased by:
a) increasing the number of turns on the . . . . ,
b) increasing the . . . . , or
c) using an . . . . core.

2 Design a relay that would use a small
current to turn **off** a big current. Draw a
labelled diagram of your design.

3 Door-chimes use an electromagnet to
make a 'bing-bong' sound. When the switch
is pushed, an iron rod hits one chime (a metal
tube). When the switch is released, the rod
springs back to hit the other chime tube.
Draw a labelled diagram to show how this
could work.

4 Design a machine that could separate full
and empty milk-bottles on a conveyor belt.

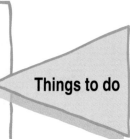

Things to do

Physics at Work

A lie detector

The diagram shows a very simple lie detector:

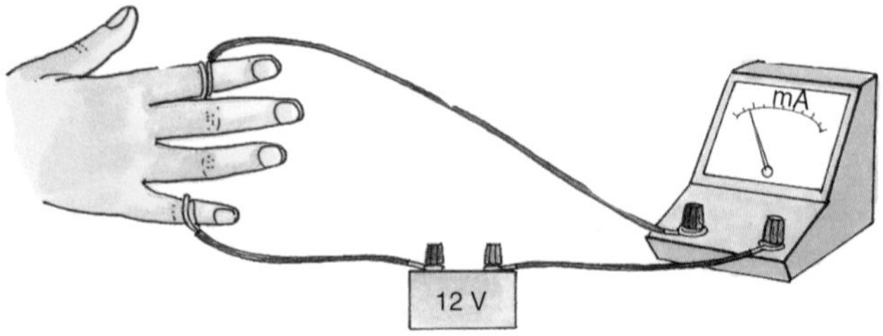

When a person tells a lie, the resistance of their skin can decrease – perhaps because they sweat with embarrassment.

a Use the words below to explain how it works.

voltage current resistance milliammeter

Car fuel gauge

Look carefully at the diagram:

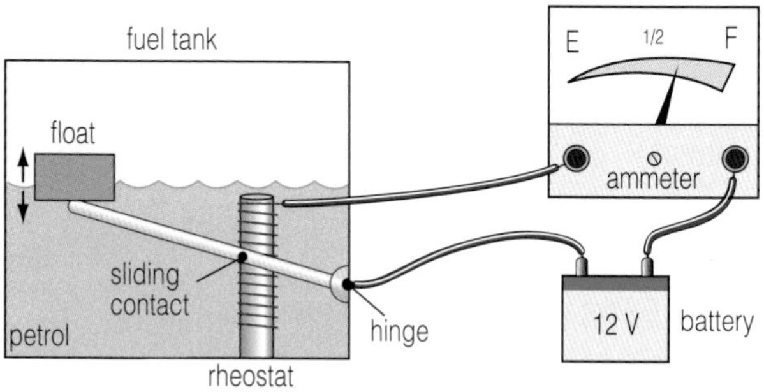

b What happens to the float as the petrol is used up?

c What does this do to the resistance of the circuit?

d How does this affect the ammeter?

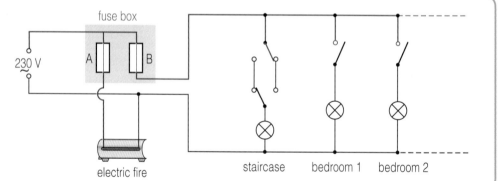

The diagram shows part of a **'mains' circuit** for a house:

e Are the lamps in series or in parallel?

f What is a fuse for?

g How does it work?

h What happens if fuse A 'blows'?

i How does the staircase circuit work?

Electric car

j Draw an Energy Transfer Diagram for this electric car.

k It has re-chargeable batteries in it. Explain how its energy probably comes from the Sun.

The Earth has a magnetic field:

l What do you notice about the shape of the field?

m Which way does a compass point?

n Near the North Pole of the Earth, is there a magnetic N-pole or S-pole?

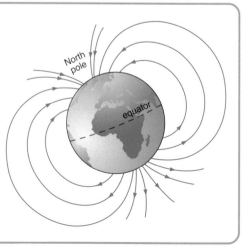

Electromagnetic relay

Analyse the diagram carefully:

o Name suitable materials for the wire of the coil, and for the core.

p Give 2 reasons why iron would be a good choice for the armature.

q Explain, step by step, what happens when the switch is closed.

r When the switch is opened, the bulb stays on. Explain why.

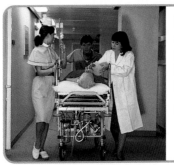

s Draw a diagram to show how a relay could be used to set off a large fireworks display safely.

t Explain how it works.

In a hospital, the corridor doors need to be open most of the time, so trolleys can move easily. But in a fire, the doors should be closed to stop the fire spreading.

u Draw a diagram to show how electromagnets can help.

Loudspeaker

The diagram shows a simple loudspeaker:

If a current is passed through the coil from A to B, the coil becomes an electromagnet and is attracted to the bar magnet.

v What happens if a current is reversed so it passes from B to A?

w What happens if the current is reversed, to and fro, 50 times in each second?
(This is called **alternating current**.)

x What difference would you hear if the current was alternating 1000 times per second?

y What difference would you hear if the current was bigger?

Microwave oven

Microwaves are dangerous, and the oven must not work while the door is open.

z Why are the 2 contact strips inside the **reed switch** made of iron?

A Why does the oven not work when the door is open?

B Why does the reed switch complete the circuit when the door is shut?

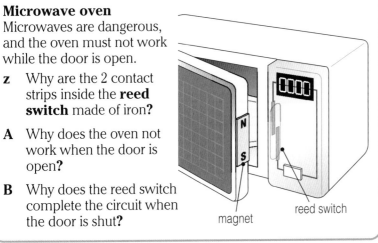

Two-tone door chime

Look at this circuit:

C Explain, step by step, how this works.

D Name a suitable material for part C.

E Which tube gives the higher note?

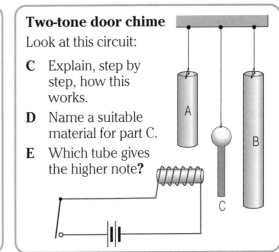

Questions

1 Benjamin Franklin (1706–1790) was a scientist who helped to write the American Declaration of Independence ("... *we hold these truths to be self-evident: that all men are created equal* ..."). He risked his life flying a kite in a storm and invented the lightning conductor.
   a) Find out all you can about him, and what he discovered.
   b) How have our ideas about electricity changed since he was alive?

Ben Franklin

2 This circuit is used to dim a light:

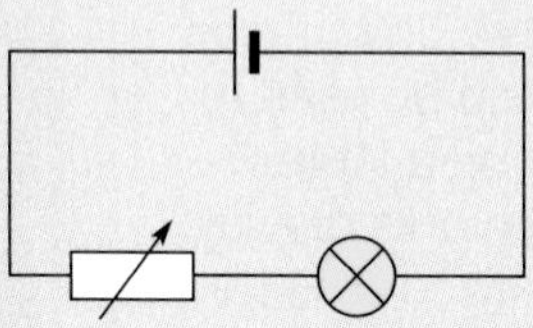

While the light is being dimmed, what happens to
   a) The current in the lamp?
   b) The resistance of the variable resistor?
   c) The voltage across the lamp?

3 The diagram shows an electrical circuit:

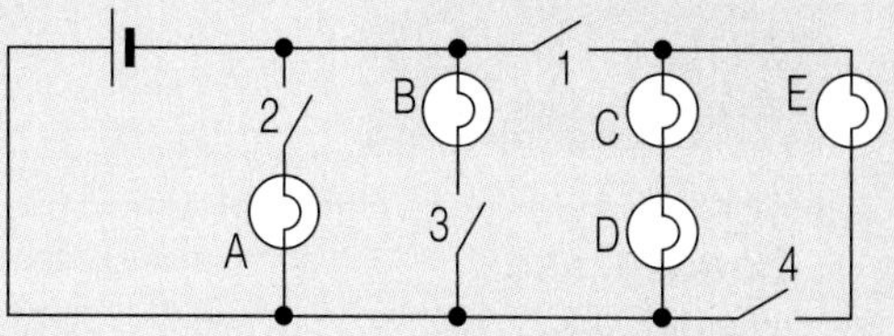

   a) What happens if only switch 1 is closed?
   b) What happens if only switches 3 and 4 are closed?
   c) How would you light bulbs A, C and D?
   d) If all the switches are closed, which bulb(s) are dimmest? Why?

4 In the circuits shown, all the cells are identical, and all the bulbs are identical:

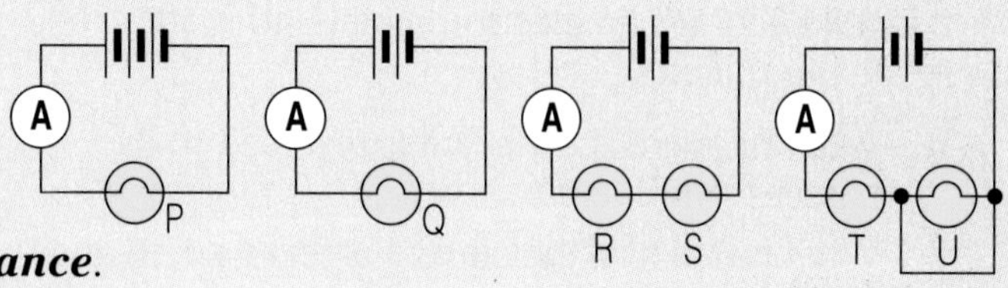

   a) Which bulb would be brightest? Why?
   b) Which bulb would not be lit? Why?
   c) Which ammeter would show the lowest reading?
      Explain why, using the words **voltage** and **resistance**.

5 Danny connected a battery in series with a switch, an ammeter, a variable resistor and a coil of wire. Then he connected a voltmeter to measure the voltage across the coil.

   a) Draw a circuit diagram of his circuit.

The table shows his results as he altered the variable resistor:

   b) Plot a large graph of the current against the voltage, drawing the line of 'best fit'.
   c) Which result(s) do you think could be wrong and should be checked?
   d) What would be the current if the voltage was 8.4 V?
   e) What conclusion(s) can you draw from the graph?

Current (A)	0.4	0.7	1.2	1.5	1.9	2.4	2.8
Voltage (V)	1.9	2.9	4.9	6.3	8.0	10.1	11.8

6 Rachel tested 2 electromagnets, one with 20 turns and one with 60 turns on the coil. She counted how many nails each electromagnet could hold up at different currents. Here are her results:

Current (A)		0	0.5	1.0	1.5	2.0	2.5	3.0	3.5	4.0
Number of nails	20-turns	0	1	4	9	15	21	27	33	38
	60-turns	0	4	12	27	42	55	61	64	64

   a) Plot a graph for each electromagnet (on the same axes).
   b) Describe what happens when the current is increased in
      i) the 20-turn coil,
      ii) the 60-turn coil.
   c) Can you explain this?

Glossary

Abrasion
When a surface is worn away by rubbing.

Absorb
When light, sound or another form of energy is taken in by something, e.g. black paper absorbs light energy, or when digested food is absorbed into the blood from the small intestine.

Acceleration
The rate at which an object speeds up.

Acid
A sour substance which can attack metal, clothing or skin. The chemical opposite of an alkali.
When an acid is dissolved in water its solution has a pH number less than 7.

Adaptation
A feature that helps a plant or an animal to survive in changing conditions.

Aerobic respiration
The process that happens in cells whereby oxygen is used to release the energy from glucose.

Agar gel
A nutritious jelly used for growing colonies of bacteria.

Air resistance
A force, due to friction with the air, which pushes against a moving object, e.g. air resistance slows down a parachute.

Alkali
The chemical opposite of an acid. A base which dissolves in water. Its solution has a pH number more than 7.

Amplitude
The size of a vibration or wave, measured from its mid-point. A loud sound has a large amplitude.

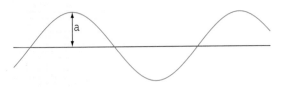

Anomalous result
A result that does not follow the general pattern in a set of data.

Antibiotic
A useful drug that helps your body fight a disease.

Atom
The smallest part of an element. All atoms contain protons and electrons.

Atomic number
The number of protons in each atom of an element. Elements are arranged in the Periodic Table in order of this atomic number.

Bacteria
Microbes made up of one cell, visible with a microscope. Bacteria can grow quickly and some of them cause disease, e.g. pneumonia.

Balanced forces
Forces are balanced when they cancel out each other. The object stays still, or continues to move at a steady speed in a straight line.

Base
The oxide, hydroxide or carbonate of a metal. (If a base dissolves in water it is called an alkali.)

Biased
Results that unfairly tend to favour one set of variables over another. For example, a survey that includes many more boys than girls when you are looking for a general pattern.

Biomass fuel
Fuel (e.g. wood) made from growing plants.

Carnivores
Animals that eat only other animals – meat-eaters.

Catalyst
A substance that alters (usually increases) the rate of a chemical reaction but is not used up so it remains chemically unchanged at the end of the reaction.

Catalytic converter
Device fitted to a car's exhaust system to reduce the pollutant gases given out.

Chemical change
A change which makes a new substance, e.g. coal burning.

Chemical energy
The energy stored in substances, e.g. foods and fuels are useful stores of chemical energy.

Chlorophyll
A green chemical in plants used to trap light energy for photosynthesis.

Chloroplasts
Tiny, round structures found inside plant cells. They capture light energy and use it to make food in photosynthesis.

Classify
To sort things out into different groups or sets.

Clone
Genetically-identical living things.

Combustion
The reaction which occurs when a substance burns in oxygen, giving out heat energy.

Community
The group of animals and plants that we find in a particular habitat.

Competition
A struggle for survival. Living things compete for scarce resources, e.g. space.

Component
One of the parts that make up an electric circuit, e.g. battery, switch, bulb.

Composition
The type and amount of each element in a compound.

Compound
A substance made when 2 or more elements are chemically joined together, e.g. water is a compound made from hydrogen and oxygen.

Conductor
An electrical conductor allows a current to flow through it. A thermal conductor allows heat energy to pass through it. All metals are good conductors.

Convection
The transfer of heat by currents in a liquid or a gas.

Dalton's atomic theory
An early theory about the composition of matter which identified an atom as the basic building block from which all substances are made.

Dispersion
The splitting of a beam of white light into the 7 colours of the spectrum, by passing it through a prism.

Displacement
When one element takes the place of another in a compound. For example,

magnesium + copper sulphate → magnesium sulphate + copper

This is called a displacement reaction.

Dissipation of energy
When energy is spread out by being transferred to lots of different places.

Drag
Friction caused by an object travelling through a liquid or gas. For example, friction caused by air resistance.

Drug
A chemical that alters the way in which your body works, e.g. alcohol, cannabis, nicotine, solvents.

Ecosystem
A group of animals and plants plus the habitat in which they are found.

Electric current
A flow of electric charges (electrons). It is measured in amps (A) by an ammeter.

Electromagnet
A coil of wire becomes a magnet when a current flows through it.

Electron
A negatively charged particle found surrounding the nucleus of an atom.

Element
A substance that is made of only one type of atom.

Endangered species
Species of plants and animals that are in danger of becoming extinct.

Endothermic
A reaction that *takes in* heat energy from the surroundings.

Enzymes
Substances which are biological catalysts. Some enzymes can speed up digestion of our food.

Epidemic
The spread of a disease through a community.

Equation
A shorthand way of showing the changes that take place in a chemical reaction

e.g.   iron + sulphur → iron sulphide
        Fe   +   S   →   FeS

Equilibrium
A balanced situation, when all the forces cancel out each other.

Evolution
Changes in the genetic composition of plants and animals over many generations so that more complex organisms develop from simpler ones.

Exothermic
A reaction that *gives out* heat energy to the surroundings.

Extinct
Species of plants and animals that have died out and no longer exist on the Earth.

Fermentation
Anaerobic fermentation is the process in which yeast converts carbohydrates, like sugars, into ethanol and carbon dioxide in the absence of air.

Carbohydrates → ethanol + carbon dioxide

Flowers
The organs that many plants use to reproduce by making seeds.

Formula
A combination of symbols to show the elements which a compound contains,
e.g. MgO is the formula for magnesium oxide.

Fossil
The remains of an animal or plant which have been preserved in rocks.

Fossil fuels
A fuel made from the remains of plants and animals that died millions of years ago, e.g. coal, oil, natural gas.

Frequency
The number of complete vibrations in each second. A sound with a high frequency has a high pitch.

Fungi
Moulds, such as yeast or mushrooms, that produce spores.

Fungicide
A chemical which kills fungi that attack crops.

Genetic engineering
The alteration of the sequence of genes in the chromosomes of a plant or animal cell by the addition of other genes.

Genes
Found in chromosomes, they control the inherited features of living things.

Gravity, gravitational force
A force of attraction between 2 objects. The pull of gravity on you is your weight.

Group
All the elements in one column down the Periodic Table.

Habitat
The place where a plant or animal lives.

Herbicide
A chemical used to kill weeds that are in competition with a crop.

Image
When you look in a mirror, you see an image of yourself.

Immune
Not being able to catch a particular disease because you have the antibodies in your blood to fight it.

Inherited
The features that are passed on from parents to their offspring.

Insulator
An electrical insulator does not allow a current to flow easily. A thermal insulator does not let heat energy flow easily.

Kinetic energy
The energy of something which is moving.

Law of reflection
When light rays bounce off a mirror:

angle of incidence = angle of reflection.

Lever
A simple machine that produces a bigger force or movement than we apply.

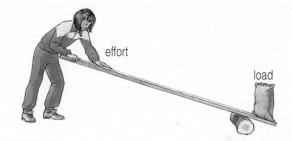

Magnetic field
The area round a magnet where it attracts or repels another magnet.

Magnetic material
A substance which is attracted by a magnet, e.g. iron and steel.

Magnify
To make bigger.

Migration
Moving from one place to another in different seasons to avoid adverse or harsh conditions.

Molecule
A group of atoms joined together.

oxygen atom

a molecule of water, H_2O

hydrogen atom

Moment
The turning effect of a force.

Moment = force × distance from the pivot.

Neutron
An uncharged particle found in the nucleus of an atom.

Opaque
An opaque object will not let light pass through it.

Oxidation
The reaction when oxygen is added to a substance.

Ozone depletion
The destruction of the ozone layer in our atmosphere. Ozone protects us from the Sun's harmful ultra-violet radiation.

Palisade cells
Cells in which most photosynthesis takes place. They are found in the upper part of a leaf.

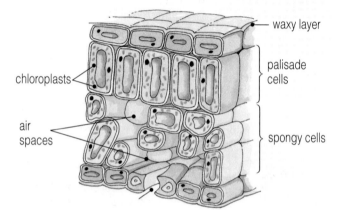

Parallel circuit
A way of connecting things in an electric circuit, so that the current divides and passes through different branches.

Pathogen
An organism that causes disease in another species, e.g. viruses or bacteria.

Period
All the elements in one row across the Periodic Table.

Periodic Table
An arrangement of elements in the order of their atomic numbers, forming groups and periods.

Pesticide
A chemical that kills insects, weeds or fungi that damage crops.

pH number
A number which shows how strong an acid or alkali is. Acids have a pH less than 7. Alkalis have a pH more than 7.

Photosynthesis
The process by which green plants use light energy to turn carbon dioxide and water into sugars:

$$\text{carbon dioxide} + \text{water} \xrightarrow[\text{chlorophyll}]{\text{light and}} \text{sugar} + \text{oxygen}$$

Physical change
A change in which no new substance is made. The substance just changes to a different state, e.g. water boiling.

Pitch
A whistle has a high pitch, a bass guitar has a low pitch.

Pollination
The transfer of pollen from the anthers to the stigma of a flower.

Population
A group of animals or plants of the same species living in the same habitat.

Potential energy
Stored energy, e.g. a bike at the top of a hill has gravitational potential energy.

Predator
An animal that hunts and eats other animals.

Pressure
A large force pressing on a small area gives a high pressure.

$$\text{Pressure} = \frac{\text{force}}{\text{area}}$$

Prey
An animal that is eaten by a predator, e.g. a rabbit is prey for the fox.

Principle of conservation of energy
The amount of energy before a transfer is always equal to the amount of energy after the transfer. The energy is 'conserved'.

Product
A substance made as a result of a chemical reaction.

Proton
A positively charged particle found in the nucleus of an atom.

Pyramid of numbers
A diagram to show how many living things there are at each level in a food chain.

Reaction
A chemical change which makes a new substance.

Reduction
A reaction when oxygen is removed, e.g. copper oxide is *reduced* to copper.

Reflection
When light bounces off an object.

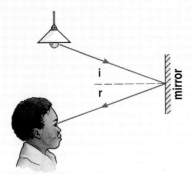

Refraction
A ray of light passing from one substance into another is bent (refracted).

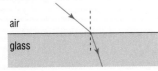

Relay
A switch that is operated by an electromagnet. A small current can switch on a large current.

Renewable energy resources
Energy sources that do not get used up, e.g. solar energy, wind, waves, tides, etc.

Resistance
A thin wire gives more resistance to an electric current than a thick wire.

Respiration
The release of energy from food in our cells. Usually using up oxygen and producing carbon dioxide.

$$\text{glucose} + \text{oxygen} \longrightarrow \text{carbon dioxide} + \text{water} + \text{energy}$$

Resultant force
The result of *unbalanced forces*.

Salt
A substance made when an acid and a base react together.

Saturated solution
A solution in which no more solute can dissolve at that temperature.

Scattering
When rays of light hit a rough surface (like paper) they reflect off in all directions.

Selective breeding
Choosing which animals and plants to breed in order to pass on useful features to the offspring, e.g. high milk yield.

Sensor
An electronic device that detects changes. It may be connected to a computer.

Series circuit
A way of connecting things in an electric circuit, so that the current flows through each one in turn.

Species
A type of living thing that breeds and produces fertile offspring.

Thermal transfer
When a cup of tea cools down, there is a transfer of thermal energy (heat) from the cup to the surroundings. This transfer can be by conduction, convection, radiation and evaporation.

Toxins
Poisons produced from bacteria and other microbes.

Unbalanced forces
If 2 forces do not cancel out each other, they are unbalanced. There will be a resultant force. The object will change its speed or change its direction.

Upthrust
Upward force produced on an object in a liquid or a gas. There is a very small upthrust in a gas.

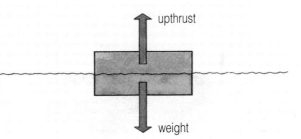

Vaccination
Protection against a disease by introducing into the body a harmless sample of the microbe that causes infection.

Variation
Differences between *different* species, e.g. between dogs and cats, or between individuals of the *same* species, e.g. people in your class.

Vibrating
Moving backwards and forwards quickly, e.g. the particles in a solid vibrate.

Viruses
Extremely small microbes which are not visible with a microscope. Many viruses spread disease by invading cells and copying themselves, e.g. influenza.

Wavelength
The distance between 2 peaks of a wave.

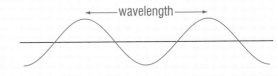

Yeast
Single-celled fungi used in the process of fermentation to make alcoholic drinks, and in bread-making.

Index